JULIA

JULIA

Reminiscences of a year in Madeleine's life as a London shop-girl

by

MRS ROBERT HENREY

LONDON
J. M. DENT & SONS LTD

First published 1971

© Mrs Robert Henrey, 1971

Made in Great Britain
at the
Aldine Press · Letchworth · Herts
for
J. M. DENT & SONS LTD
Aldine House · Bedford Street · London

ISBN: 0 460 03920 2

I

THE morning was dark and uninviting. Rain fell lightly. It must have done this in a peevish, desultory way for most of the night, with the result that the streets were now wet, black and shiny. Julia reflected with resignation that weather like this was a bad omen, and that by the time she arrived her light shoes would be soaked and there would be mud on her stockings right up to her calves. 'I won't have time to change them,' she told herself. 'The best thing will be to run straight up to the Ladies and try washing the mud off without taking them off.' She had bought three pairs in order to take advantage of a slight reduction in price, and though she usually was not easily pleased with what she did, this piece of business appeared to have been wise.

She had taken this short cut through narrow, unfamiliar streets to save a long wait in the rain in a queue, the scramble to get on the bus and the bus fare, but it now was obvious that she was going to arrive late. The streets she hurried along were lined with grubby but endearing small shops of a kind that were disappearing quickly from the heart of London's West End. There were furriers and fur cold storage warehouses, button manufacturers, kosher butchers, music publishers and even an occasional dairy. Litter from street-traders' barrows added to the mud in the gutters. Unless she had miscalculated, she should emerge at any moment into Kingly Street. There was a church that gave the impression of being let into the side of a brick wall, and then the backs of all those great department stores whose brilliantly lit plate glass façades turned the east side of Regent Street into a perpetual fairyland.

From the time she had left school it had been Julia's dream to work in this one particular store filled with artificial sunshine, beautiful dresses and exotic perfume. Through this enrichment of her experience, she would walk with assurance, her head held high, into the greater opportunities of a sophisticated world.

She had not expected an answer to her written application for the job. Still less had she expected a favourable outcome to the interview at which she had found herself one of more than a dozen girls who had looked at each other with distrust, if not actual dislike. Fortunately she had caught sight of Daisy crossing the room with a pile of letters. Daisy, singling her out from the other girls, had discreetly waved and smiled to encourage her. Daisy lived with her parents in a basement flat in the same street off Charing Cross Road in which Julia and her mother lodged. Daisy's dream was to be some important man's private secretary. She was twenty, ambitious and wished to see the world. Her position in this store by no means gave her the same feeling of elation that Julia had when she thought about her coming association with it. In Julia's estimation, Daisy was a lucky girl. Luck is a thing to envy.

'Nine o'clock!'

The man seated at the deal table had a large watch in his right hand. With his left hand he wrote down the name of each arrival and the corresponding time of arrival.

'The hour hasn't struck yet,' Julia objected.

'By nine you should be ready in your department waiting for the first customers,' he said. 'As it is, you'll not be there till nine-fifteen. So, you're late!'

Passing through the great store, she caught sight of her mud-flaked stockings reflected in one great mirror after another, and she regretted not having queued up for a bus. She had been assigned to 'Artificial Flowers', where a salesgirl had started with delicate, airy gestures to pass round the merchandise with a small feather duster. From time to time this girl would go to a drawer, choose a buttercup or a rose,

6

make it stand up artistically against a thin copper support, and then stand back to admire the effect.

'I just wonder,' she said, suddenly noticing Julia, 'what made them assign you to my department. I've grown accustomed, these past few weeks, to working alone. In any case, they need an extra girl in the basement this morning to help with the parcels. I'm to send you down right away.'

'Would you mind if I left my handbag in this drawer with your own?' asked Julia. 'As I shall be working here.'

Her companion, overcoming her desire to be agreeable, said softly:

'No, really. I would honestly prefer you to take it down to the basement with you. Another girl's handbag is a responsibility I hate to burden myself with. You do understand?'

'Yes, I suppose so. I'll take it with me. Will you tell me how to get to this place where they make up the parcels? I feel a bit lost this morning.'

'You'll find some stairs just behind that show case with the silk scarves and costume jewellery. Go down one flight. Ask the first person you meet. You just can't go wrong.' She paused before returning to the subject that had so visibly aggrieved her. 'I can't get over the fact that they are sending you to work with me on your first day. Girls are not generally sent straight to a department to serve customers. By the way, how old are you?'

'Seventeen,' said Julia.

'Oh!' exclaimed her companion. 'Seventeen.'

'How old are you?'

Julia's companion dismissed this question as impertinent. Bending over the heavy drawer built into the counter, she selected an artificial azalea flower. Dismissing Julia from her mind, she placed the green wired stem between her teeth and, taking up the feather duster, raised her right arm in an elegant curve. Now her duster passed lightly here and there while her feet executed what appeared to be a ballet of her own.

. . . . . .

7

Too excited to be resentful and too full of expectation, Julia discovered the stairs and went thoughtfully down the uncarpeted flight to the basement. Here she found herself in the room where some days earlier she and the other candidates had gathered for their interviews. How nervous she had been! It was kind of Daisy to have given her that smile, that little wave of encouragement.

This large, almost unfurnished room led into others. In one of these she came upon a collection of wax mannequins, some without legs or arms, their small round heads bald as if shaved; others superb with wigs of human hair, lips parted in a perpetual smile, big, round eyes unblinking under long, beautiful lashes. These stood nakedly awaiting the moment when, dressed in all the prettiest and most alluring clothes, they would be removed under cover of night, when most of the city was asleep, Julia supposed, to their accustomed places behind those plate glass windows facing Regent Street. Julia stood for a moment and silently contemplated the beauty of these models destined to spend half their lives in the shade, half in the glare of arc-lamps. By stretching out an arm (she was short-sighted) she could lightly touch their swan-like necks, their small, firm breasts, their tiny waists, the smooth roundness of their hips. What man, she wondered, faced by such perfection would ever have eyes for a girl as imperfectly proportioned as she felt herself to be? She was obsessed by a number of flaws in her youthful body, flaws that, increasingly of late, corroded her moments of happiness: the slimness of her shoulders, for instance, and, in spite of long, shapely legs, rather wide hips. It struck her as being monstrously unfair that a wax model could attain perfection so much more easily than a human girl. Only the breath of life was missing. Turning on her heels she suddenly noticed a huge mirror in which these nude mannequins were reflected an infinite number of times, and beside them, equally reflected more times than she could count, herself, such a surprising herself in her little black dress with the long sleeves, her honey blonde hair, her delicate neck and her eyes which, though small, had a

8

strange capacity for changing colour. On rainy mornings they were grey. When the sun shone they were blue as the sea. Her nose, she decided, was a good point, small and humorous, and her teeth when she laughed, which was often, were like pearls.

Adventuring a little farther, she came into a room where two men wearing slate-coloured dust coats were consulting a large chart. Their voices were raised in heated argument. Julia wondered if she dared to interrupt them. Her colleague in Artificial Flowers had said: 'Ask the first person you meet.' Unhappily, Julia thought how fortunate the wax mannequins were not to have to deal with problems like this. The basement was unheated and she was cold in her black dress. She now noticed in another part of the room a dark-haired girl, very small and slight, busily writing at a table covered with booklets and papers. Going over to her, Julia said:

'Excuse me, but I have been sent down to help in Despatch.'

'Oh, no!' cried the girl, throwing up her head and laughing. 'You too? For more than a fortnight I have been imprisoned every morning between two men who only talk to each other and a roomful of wax mannequins who never speak to anybody.' She drew a spare chair beside her and added: 'Come and sit down.'

Julia sat down, put her handbag in front of her and said: 'I thought I was to tie up parcels. What are you doing?'

'Writing the names and addresses of our regular customers on these envelopes so that we can send them the new catalogue. I've reached the letter G. "Mrs Green of Pretty Sea View, Eastbourne." What do you think Mrs Green looks like? Is she young or old, dark or fair, and what is she wearing at this moment? By the way, what's your name?'

'Julia, and I am seventeen.'

'I'm Edith and I'm twenty-three. How lovely to have somebody to talk to! Have you seen the catalogue?' She handed one to Julia. 'Have a look!'

'I don't think I should,' said Julia. 'This is my first day.'

'Personally,' said Edith, 'I know the catalogue by heart. If I had nothing else to do but address envelopes all morn-

9

ing, I'd go mad. But looking at the catalogue allows me to buy in imagination what is inside. This dress, for instance. Fabulous, don't you think? I chose it while half way through the C's last Thursday morning. And this one? It would be lovely to wear for a dance. Between ourselves I shall end by buying everything!' Turning suddenly on Julia she enquired anxiously:

'Have you a boy-friend?'

'Not yet. I suppose you have?'

'I?' said Edith. 'Dozens!'

She laughed and a great warmth lit up her beautiful dark eyes. Her skin was like polished olive wood and her jet black hair shone with streaks of reflected light. Under ample breasts, that could obviously dispense with padding in her bra, her waist was softly slim. 'Oh!' thought Julia. 'Never have I seen a young woman so clearly made for love. No wonder she has dozens of boy-friends.'

These reflections were not of a kind to help Julia appreciate the task of addressing envelopes. After a few moments she laid down her pen and asked:

'Are we going to wade through the entire alphabet?'

'No,' answered Edith, only too ready to talk, 'as a matter of fact we have something quite different to do tomorrow morning. That may be the reason they sent you down from your department to help me. Have you ever tried to make creases disappear from tissue paper?'

'Tissue paper doesn't often come my way,' said Julia. 'Not the really good kind, crisp and white.'

'Well,' said Edith, 'take a look at all those parcels stacked in the far corner of the room. They contain the goods returned by difficult, dissatisfied customers. Our job is to unpack the parcels carefully, take the contents back to the store room, keep the white cardboard boxes, and then try to take the creases out of the tissue paper wrapping. Tissue paper is fabulously valuable. Did you know that? We must try to smooth it out till it looks like new.'

Edith sighed.

'Oh, these married women with their complexes! The

Mrs Browns and the Mrs Greens who write saying: "My husband didn't like me in the yellow dress!" Husbands! You have no idea how frightened the firm is of husbands! The very word makes the management give in. "The two-piece I bought yesterday looked quite different when I tried it on at home," they say. Can you imagine all the family looking on!' Edith smiled. 'I'm in the dress department. I know.'

'I'm in Artificial Flowers,' said Julia.

'Yes, of course, at seventeen you are far too young to be put in a really important department. Personally I adore model dresses. But because I'm still only a junior sales-woman I only get the customers that the others don't want. Afternoons are not too bad but we are seldom busy in the mornings. The senior saleswomen think they can manage alone. That explains why I have been lent to Despatch here for the past fortnight.'

'What do you do during the lunch hour?' asked Julia, wondering if her new friend went home. Edith answered:

'I have a quick sandwich and a cup of coffee. Then I spend the rest of my lunch hour wandering along Regent Street and Oxford Street looking into the windows. I compare all the great stores. Occasionally I work myself up into such a state of excitement that I end by wanting to exterminate all the other stores between Marble Arch and Piccadilly Circus. Imagine! If all the women who wanted to buy dresses were obliged to come here I would be needed in the department all the morning, and I wouldn't have to come down to this basement again. I love the gilded mirrors and the bright lights, the soft carpets and the eager look on the faces of all those women who come into the store full of hope. My dream would be to marry a man who had enough money to open a store of his own. My head is crammed full of ideas. First of all, of course, before I left this place I would sack the buyer.'

At this thought Edith broke into a peal of laughter.

During all this time the two men had gone on discussing in deep, earnest voices the chart so importantly laid out in front of them on their own table. Now they pushed their chairs back at the sound of the girls' laughter and condescendingly advanced towards them.

'May we know the cause of this hilarity?' asked one, a young man Julia thought quite handsome.

'Of course,' answered Edith. 'It's simple. I was just imagining I'd married a young man wealthy enough to buy a store of his own, a store as large as this one. Before leaving I had sacked the buyer of our dress department. Don't you think that's funny?'

'Very funny,' answered the young man pompously. 'Meanwhile it would be better for you both to go on addressing envelopes. How do you suppose my colleague and I can plan next week's window displays if we are to be disturbed all the time by your schoolgirl giggling?'

'I'm not a schoolgirl,' said Edith. 'I've had two weeks experience as a junior salesgirl in the dress department. I have learnt a great deal. Besides, as it happens, window displays interest me particularly. Incidentally, this is Julia. She is new today.'

Something had been running through Julia's mind. Looking up into the eyes of the young man whom she considered the handsomer of the two, she asked:

'Is it you who dress the naked mannequins before placing them in the window?'

'You're very inquisitive for a new girl,' he said. 'Take care that you and your girl-friend don't both get sacked instead of planning how to sack the buyer in the dress department.'

'Seriously,' asked Edith. 'What are you planning to make them wear?'

As soon as the two men were back working at their own table, Edith whispered to Julia:

'When I was here alone I would never have dared speak to them. It's extraordinary what two girls together can do. Honestly, I think you made the younger one blush. Just because you were sitting beside me I never felt shy for a single moment. The same when I go dancing. I always try to go with another girl and even if she finds a partner before I do, it's better to be two than one. On the whole, at dances, I am pretty lucky. Do you like dancing?'

'I adore it,' said Julia, 'but mother dislikes me going out on my own. I have to be careful. Besides, mother is a widow and I have a conscience. It's not fair to leave her by herself too often in the evening.'

'I have no worries on that score,' said Edith. 'I have left home and I will never go back. I'm not a London girl. I had to fight to get here but, now I am here, London is my town. I love every inch of it, and I don't think I could live anywhere else, except perhaps New York. Or maybe Paris? Or Rome? I suppose I could get to like any great city in which there are stores as wonderful as this one.'

'How dreadful to have cut yourself off from your parents!' exclaimed Julia, thinking of the closeness between herself and her mother. 'Don't you ever write to them?'

'No,' said Edith, 'not even at Christmas.'

She paused.

'When I get married I will write. Yes, I will write to announce my wedding. And, as my husband will be rich, I will send them a cheque for a sum multiplied by eighteen, the number of years I cost them my keep.'

Her expression had lost all its gaiety. Her brow was sombre, her voice low but explosively violent.

'That,' she said, 'will be, as far as my parents are concerned, the end.'

The windowless basement with its tall, dusty rooms, its deal tables and hard chairs, its narrow corridors and silences, the arms and torsos of wax figures lying on the cold, cement floor now gave Julia the impression of being imprisoned in a crypt. Death, not life, seemed to prevail. But though all that was fresh and tender in her nature had received a shock, and she ought, she told herself, to rise in revolt against the apparent harshness of Edith's attitude towards her parents, nothing but pity and affection welled up inside her. She had known Edith for only little more than an hour. In spite of this Edith had become her friend. There are loyalties. Instinct told her that she and Edith would ride together into the unknown. Circumstances had prevented her from forming the sort of friendships that some girls accumulate during their teens. This then was the beginning of a new experience and, on her return home this evening, she would recount it in detail to her mother who, being so little older than she was (only nineteen years separated them) and yet infinitely wiser, would help her analyse every seemingly insignificant word. Even as this prospect passed through Julia's mind, Edith changed. The cynical girl with the sombre brow was once again gay, mordant, irrepressible. 'How beautiful she is!' thought Julia as Edith, with a quick toss of her jet black hair, gathered the catalogues and envelopes into bundles.

'We have to take them to the General Office,' she explained to Julia. 'If you come with me you'll be able to cast your jealous eyes over all those young secretaries and typists who consider themselves so vastly superior to salesgirls like us. Shall I tell you why? It's not that they know shorthand and can type. Or at least, not only that. Though I must say one or two of them flourish their pencils and notebooks as if they had written last month's Best Seller. No, the reason is that whereas we salesgirls are obliged to wear our little black dresses, they can wear the clothes they like. You'll see. Most of them go about in tweed skirts and bright jerseys or blouses.'

Edith laughed cruelly.

'Watch how I treat them.'

'Oh, no,' Julia implored, thinking of Daisy and how kind Daisy had been to her. 'Not all of them are superior and proud. I happen to know one. She lives in the same street as mother and me, and she's quite brilliant. Her mother is convinced she has a great future.'

'All mothers think that about their daughters,' said Edith sharply.

The girls, their bundles finally made up, nodded to the two men who were still at work on their chart and hurried off, their heels ringing on the cement floor. In an office filled with girls typing, Edith went over to a young woman dressed in a tweed skirt and an orange jumper.

'This is Julia, a new girl from Artificial Flowers,' she said. 'We have been doing some more catalogues, but I must say that some of your entries in the address book are scarcely legible. Somebody could take more care.'

Where was Daisy?

Julia looked around, fearing her companion would raise her voice, but Edith's barb about somebody's handwriting went no further, and the young secretary in the orange jumper merely smiled. As they left the office, Edith whispered:

'Did you notice how I gave her a piece of my mind? Now, let's go to the Ladies, and then lunch.'

Really, thought Julia, there's no stopping Edith. How fortunate I am to have hit on such a dynamic girl for my first real friend! She is positively organizing me!

While the two girls stood side by side at the basins, Edith started to hum a dance tune about the night having a thousand eyes.

'Do you suppose,' she asked, suddenly breaking off, 'that the thousand eyes stand for a thousand stars? I never thought of that before. I try to memorize lines from all the latest dance tunes and afterwards I mull over them trying to understand the real sense. I used to have a boy-friend who claimed it showed a retrograde tendency, that it proved I was a slow reactor.' She laughed: 'Little did he know me!'

Edith was talking and laughing into the mirror in front of her while Julia was washing the ink off her hands. A young woman came quickly through the door and the scene suddenly changed. Edith's figure seemed to tense and her laughter died away. Without taking any notice of the two girls, the young woman went straight to her locker, took something out of it and then disappeared into one of the toilets. Edith whispered to her companion:

'Quick! Let's go! She's my boss—the buyer of the dress department, the one I was going to sack if ever I marry a man who buys me a store. She might split on me for going

15

off to lunch twenty minutes before time. You can never trust these older women.'

'For Heaven's sake,' said Julia in the same low voice, 'that young woman is not old. Why, she is probably ten years younger than my mother, and my mother appears so young that people take us in the street for sisters. I thought her terribly elegant.'

'Elegant, yes,' whispered Edith, putting careful touches to her make-up, 'but that is just the point. One never appears really elegant until one is nearing thirty, and thirty is what I call old. The head of my department, for instance, is twenty-nine. You should hear how she nags me: "Watch the way that dress falls, Edith. Can't you see it has a flared skirt?" "Edith, I saw you with that customer while she was trying on the little peach number. You should have been more careful with her hair. Never allow a dress to disarrange a customer's hair-do!" "Oh, Edith, see what you have done! Could you not have prevented that customer from putting lipstick on the white piqué collar of my latest navy blue model!" That is how she goes on all day until closing time. Are you surprised that I hate her?'

Edith turned her head sharply in the direction of the toilet where her unseen enemy had just pulled the chain. It was as if Edith had, out of devilry, waited for this moment to make a sign to her friend and then hurriedly escape. Julia seized her handbag and followed the madcap girl. Side by side, feeling slightly guilty but proud of themselves, they hurried out into the street.

The sun breaking out from behind the last fleecy clouds was turning this wide, graceful stretch of Regent Street into a joyful, shimmering picture of silver and gold. Julia, short-sighted, blinked. She felt momentarily blinded by the light, deafened by the low, ceaseless roar. Shining cars, taxis, vans, scarlet two-decker buses were seemingly locked together in the centre of the mighty, curving way, while lunch-hour crowds, mostly women, milled along the pavements that were by now dry and hot. Julia's new stockings, restored to perfect sheen, and the sharp click of her heels made her feel

16

light and airy. Above the noise of the traffic and the voices of passers-by rose the well-loved though metallic strains of an old music-hall favourite. It was being played jerkily and far too quickly on a veteran street organ by its owner, who, evidently defeated by the blatant prosperity of the time, displayed his war medals on a frayed suit. A Salvation Army lass shook a collection box; an old man sold coloured balloons. Here, with all its contrasts, was the London Julia loved. Edith, excitable and light-footed, almost danced ahead and turned round to call out to Julia:

'Isn't Regent Street fabulous? Streets are what I like. Streets are magic. In the town where I was born there were crowds, but they lacked life and colour, and before one had gone a dozen yards one was sure to meet somebody one knew, and then the mystery disappeared. The fun of a great shopping crowd is to feel one with it but to know nobody!'

She suddenly swivelled round and stood as if transfixed in front of a plate glass window.

'Look!' she cried. 'Just look at that gorgeous coat!'

Expertly, she started to point out what was particularly clever about it. The collar, in her estimation, was most cunningly designed. For a girl with a swan-like neck it would be shatteringly effective. Julia agreed there was something unusually clever about the cut of the collar, but she admitted that if Edith had not pointed this out to her, she might never have noticed what in particular was so new and interesting about it. She felt that her lack of experience weighed against her.

Two young girls with slim figures and soft dark eyes had detached themselves from the slowly moving crowd and now stood between Julia and Edith. They also had been attracted by the coat. Both of them began to dissect its defects and its qualities, one not liking the sleeve, the other questioning the height of the belt and the choice of buttons. But both agreed that there was something noteworthy about the collar. When they had gone, Julia said to her friend:

'Did you hear what they said? They didn't particularly

like the sleeves but they confirmed your opinion about the collar.'

'How on earth do you know?' asked Edith. 'They weren't talking English.'

'They were Italian,' said Julia. 'There are several Italian families in our street. Mother and I have no difficulty in understanding them.'

'Congratulations,' said Edith. 'I never guessed you were so clever!'

Julia blushed at the compliment. She felt that this small success would prove to be one of the nicest things about her day. Soon they were back in front of their own store, examining selfconsciously the lovely things—the lingerie, the dresses, the perfumes, the gloves, the furs, the handbags displayed there. They were selfconscious because they already formed part of the store. Edith said: 'To be seen admiring the wonders of the store where one works is like being recognized by one's parents when out walking with a boy-friend!'

The girls finally parted, each going to her own department. Julia experienced again that feeling of loneliness that had come over her earlier in the day. As soon as her colleague in Artificial Flowers sighted her, she exclaimed:

'Oh! There are several things you simply will have to learn, like relieving another girl at exactly the right time. You are at least three minutes late and I am starving.'

Pulling out the drawer in which she kept her handbag, she proceeded to go through the motions of a salesgirl going off to lunch, and said:

'You are not likely to be disturbed much before I am back at two o'clock. The afternoon rush seldom starts before three. If you take my advice, you will have a careful look round the department to get accustomed to the flowers and the prices.'

As Julia watched her colleague disappear she was appalled at the weight of responsibility on her frail shoulders. However small this department might be compared with the one where Edith worked, Julia was, nevertheless, in sole charge of it. She must brace herself. Supposing she did make a sale, how would she write out the bill? Where did her colleague keep the book for this purpose? After a while she discovered it under a spray of mimosa. Then she panicked because she had no pencil, searching wildly for one until she remembered that there was always a pencil tucked into the leather binding of the sales book. She looked round at what she could see of the rest of the store, wondering if there was anything in a customer's face to betray an urgent desire to buy a narcissus or a rose. If she were not so frightened she would *will* a customer to come her way. Sister Angelica had told the girls in Convent that only prayer could overcome intense fear. Prayer, Sister Angelica said, gave girls courage. Behind a curtain of nasturtiums, Julia silently made a remembered prayer, and suddenly out of the misty unknown appeared a customer asking the price of a bunch of violets. Julia read it off the tab. The customer lost interest and walked smartly away. Why did the woman go away without buying it? What had Julia done wrong? Was she going to prove herself a failure during this hour she had been left alone?

Julia wandered disconsolately from bouquet to bouquet. A new possibility struck her. Had she misread the price of the violets? She took them up again and scrutinized the tab. There had been no mistake. Short-sighted girls tend to read with accuracy what they can hold close to their eyes just as they are often gentler in their movements than long-sighted girls; this was something her mother had always impressed on her. Perhaps she should have engaged her potential customer in conversation at once so that she could discover a common interest?

An old man, slight of build, with blue eyes and white hair, came along pushing a large, square osier basket on wheels. He bade her a very civil good afternoon, and added in a soft, friendly voice:

'Are you a new girl?'

'Yes,' she answered, touched by his kindness.

'Your first day?'

19

'Yes.'

'I could tell,' he said, bringing his osier trolley to a halt beside her. 'I always can tell. It's written all over your face. Shy? A bit nervous? Don't worry. It will pass. By the end of the week you will be chirping like a London sparrow. New girls! I have seen dozens, hundreds, in my time. The prettier they are, the less time they stay with us. It seems they are hard to satisfy.'

'Oh!' cried Julia. 'But I am different! I want to stay— only I am scared!'

The old man smiled.

'So long!' he said. 'You will see me again. I push my trolley from department to department collecting parcels for Despatch. Backwards and forwards like the proverbial ferryman. Mind, I meet lots of people. My life is a gay one and each day passes far too quickly. Goodbye, little girl!'

'Goodbye!' said Julia.

A young woman had stopped to look at a bunch of gardenias. Julia went up softly to her and said:

'Aren't they pretty?'

'Yes,' said the young woman, 'they are pretty but I would need three to make a diadem on my hair.'

'Oh!' exclaimed Julia, 'that would be gorgeous! Are you going to a dance?'

Dancing was Julia's idea of bliss.

'I am to be a bridesmaid at my sister's wedding,' explained the young woman, 'so I am beginning to buy what I shall need week by week, but I am not at all sure of myself. I hesitate a lot and, as the only time I have for shopping is in my lunch hour, I spend most of it in dreamy indecision.' She looked into Julia's eager, young face and asked nervously: 'Do you really think three would be enough?'

Julia chose three of the prettiest. She placed them gently against the young woman's auburn hair and led her in front of a medallion-shaped mirror, saying:

'See for yourself how well they suit you! Aren't they lovely?'

'Yes,' agreed the young woman, 'they are lovely, and I

am so happy that you should convince me. It is wonderful to have the opinion of another girl. When I am left to myself I can so seldom reach a decision. Please do them up for me.'

Julia chose a small white cardboard box and lovingly placed the three gardenias in a soft bed of tissue paper. Then, as calmly as if she had done it all her life, she made out a bill for her customer to take to the cash desk.

She had made her first sale! What a confusion of excitement, what a galaxy of faces—Sister Angelica so well remembered, Edith, her new friend, the two Italian girls in Regent Street, the dignified young secretary in her tweed skirt and orange jumper, the shy, endearing customer buying three gardenias to wear when she acted as a bridesmaid at her sister's wedding.

A girl in a black dress like Julia's came up to her and asked in a low voice if her name was Julia.

'Yes,' Julia answered with sudden apprehension.

'Edith has sent me to say that if she misses you during the tea-break will you please meet her in Regent Street after work. She will come as soon as she can. Bye-bye. I must not get caught so far from my base.'

Swiftly the girl disappeared. True enough, Edith had vaguely talked about meeting Julia in the Ladies during the twenty-minute tea-break, but as their times would probably not coincide, she had decided on a more dependable rendezvous.

Julia was now sufficiently sure of herself to move cautiously beyond the limits of her own department, and as she did so she came face to face with a cashier in her gilded cage. Julia examined her as an explorer might examine something strange in the jungle. The cashier appeared a redoubtable person, the top of her head appearing above hidden reserves of jingling money. Her hair was henna-dyed and piled up high in the form of a sugar loaf.

'Hello, new girl!' said the cashier, looking up from the silver coins she was counting.

They eyed each other with mutual interest. Julia decided

that the cashier was probably about thirty-five, but though her shoulders and arms had thickened, her blue eyes were lively and full of fun. The gay cashier was adorned by a vivid necklace and a large topaz brooch pinned on her shoulder. Her coquetry was clearly concentrated on her hair, her bust and her hands, since the rest of her was invisible for so much of the day.

'Oh dear,' said the cashier. 'Will it never be two o'clock! I'm longing to stretch my legs.'

She gave Julia a wide, friendly smile.

'Are you happy here?'

'Oh, yes!' exclaimed Julia with such a burst of enthusiasm that the cashier was quite taken aback. 'Aren't you?'

'I might be if it weren't Monday,' said the cashier. 'By this evening, of course, after one whole day has been nibbled off the working week, I may feel better. The fact is that money disgusts me. The more I handle the less I seem to earn. Besides, the stuff is downright filthy. These notes are so greasy that I have to keep on washing my hands and the coins chip off and discolour my nail varnish. By the way, don't appear to be talking to me and keep an eye on your department. This place is full of spies. It is you I am thinking about, not me. They would never dare get rid of me. No girl of your age would submit to being locked up in a cage all day unable to dance on her toes. The young girls want to be up and about. Not that I am as old as you probably think I am. At your age one thinks anybody over the age of twenty ancient, but I do have a husband and a son of fourteen, and that makes a difference. At my age one thinks less about dancing than about paying one's mortgage on the house. Ah! Now at last I can go to lunch.'

Her relief stood waiting for her to vacate the cage. As the cashier stepped down, Julia noticed that she was small and stout and her handbag, which she held by the strap, beat against a bulging calf. She looked better in the cage than out of it.

The clock, which had struck two, also brought Julia's

colleague back from her lunch. Julia watched her slipping her handbag back in her drawer. After this the girl stood in front of the flower stand, arms crossed, waiting.

'Did you make a sale?' she asked.

'Three gardenias,' answered Julia.

'Let us hope the customer does not bring them back to you tomorrow!' said her companion. 'Lunch-hour sales are never any good. Secretaries and typists buy things in a hurry, and just as soon as they are back in the office they can't resist showing what they have bought to the other girls who start tearing everything apart like a lot of cats! You'll soon see. Your customer will come back with her gardenias tomorrow, and you will either have to exchange them for something else, or arrange for her to get her money back.'

She had scarcely spat her venom than, like sunshine after a storm, she suddenly became all suppleness, all sweetness, all smiles. Her words had left Julia too deflated, too ready to lament the shattering of the fairy tale she had woven round the gardenias and the bridesmaid, to notice the arrival of an elegant customer who was admiring a small headdress of coloured feathers in a showcase. Julia's colleague, scenting an exceptional sale, radiated such enthusiasm and charm that she had suddenly become beautiful. The curve of her mouth, austere when she had spoken to Julia, had become round and soft, and the slight flush colouring her cheeks set off admirably the natural waviness of her hair.

'No,' said the customer gently, as Julia's colleague offered to open the show case. 'The feathers are enchanting, but I'm looking for a present for a young niece and I hardly think she would have any occasion to wear them. This little thing with tulle would be more appropriate.'

Julia's colleague was delighted by her sale.

'Did you hear?' she asked Julia as soon as the customer had gone. 'It was a present for her niece. I took the price off before wrapping it up in a gift box so there will be no question of her bringing it back. Experience will teach you little tricks like that. One must take precautions. By the way, did I tell you my name? I am Elizabeth. People call me Betty. I would have preferred to be called Veronica.'

'Oh,' exclaimed Julia, 'Betty is a lovely name, and Elizabeth is so regal!'

She caught herself blushing at the directness of the compliment, wondering if the suddenly humanized Betty would not think her schoolgirlish and naïve. Julia and her mother read too many novels. There was always a danger of this, she often told herself, in this widowed mother-daughter relationship. It was liable to produce problems of a rather special kind. At the moment she treated her mother almost as a contemporary, as a girl-friend rather than as an older woman. Perhaps if there was something wide-eyed and childish about Julia, it might come from her closeness to a relatively young mother who in her daughter's absence led a solitary, dreamlike existence.

How old-fashioned could a girl remain in a modern, scientific world? How different could a minority be from the accepted notion of modern girls? On this first afternoon Julia was convinced that a Prince Charming would some day appear searching for her amongst the feathers and the flowers. Such beliefs were best kept to oneself. One should not boast about a lack of disenchantment.

Betty was touched by Julia's compliment about her name, and happy to have made a sale. Too young and too attractive to bear a grudge for long, she was now anxious to win Julia over as a friend.

'One is never quite sure with a new face,' she explained, 'and then again Monday is a bad day. Young married customers have a tendency to stay at home to recover from the exhaustion of having their men with them over the weekend. Husbands are a pleasant necessity, but they upset the routine.'

The store, in spite of this, was beginning to fill up. In her efforts to be nice Betty went as far as to say that though at first she had mildly resented Julia's arrival, yet her appointment to the department re-established Betty as its head. To be head of a department showed that one had an assistant.

24

There might be minor advantages in running a department all by oneself, but seniority was important. Having a staff, even of one, impressed the management.

'Normally we should be two,' said Betty, 'but the girl they gave me before left to get married.'

'Where did she meet her husband?' asked Julia immediately. This seemed to her the vital point.

'Here in the store,' said Betty, 'right under my nose and, what do you think, I had never even noticed him.'

'Oh!' cried Julia, 'so it can happen!'

'It did happen. What vexed me was that he might just as easily have chosen me!'

'But if you were not expecting him?' objected Julia. 'One has to believe in it.'

'Nonsense,' said Betty, not divining Julia's raid into fairy-tale land, 'and anyway I would not have wanted him.'

'Why not?'

'Because as soon as he married her, he took her to Canada, and I don't want to go to Canada.'

'It sounds wonderful!' said Julia. 'Being taken off to Canada.'

'We all subscribed to give her a wedding present,' went on Betty, 'but she did not invite a single one of us to the church.' She added dreamily: 'She was married in white. We would have liked to share her happiness. How about you? Have you a boy-friend yet?'

'No,' said Julia. 'I go out so little, because I live with my widowed mother.'

A smart young woman with a beautiful hair-do and obviously very sure of herself was approaching their department. Tall, in the early thirties, there was something of the professional woman about her, the successful career girl. The moment Betty caught sight of her she hurried across to meet her, having whispered to Julia: 'There is Mrs Davies, our buyer.' They exchanged a few words and then Betty brought Mrs Davies over to Julia to introduce her. The older woman looked the young girl up and down, expressed the hope that she might develop into a good salesgirl, then asked:

'Where were you this morning? I did not see you.'
Betty answered quickly on her behalf:
'She was sent to help another girl in Despatch.'
'I understand!'

Her quick, intelligent eyes flicked round the pretty merchandise that made this department one of the most colourful in the store, then came to rest on the more expensive items in the showcase.

'We must find some way to dispose of those feather headpieces,' she said. 'I paid far too much for them and they are so delicate that they will end by losing their freshness. Try to think something up.'

She laughed, a beautiful warm, throaty laugh. It was the laugh of a happy woman, thought Julia, a woman who has a husband, and maybe children at home.

'So long!' she said benevolently, enveloping the two girls in an almost tender look.

The store began to get busy. Julia found herself wrapping up a spray of violets for a girl who had chosen them on her own. Betty described this phase as the rush hour before the tea hour. 'When the shop is crowded,' she explained, 'customers excite one another into buying by the very fact that there are so many of them. They fear that unless they make up their minds quickly, others will come up behind them and seize the prize. On the other hand, when the store is empty, it needs a lot of persuasion to make a customer buy.'

An elegant woman who looked as if she might have stepped out of a Rolls-Royce approached Betty, speaking to her in an accent that Julia supposed was Spanish or Portuguese. After a few moments Betty went to the special showcase and took out, with the precautions that a nurse might employ to take a premature baby out of an incubator, the most delicate of those plumed headdresses that Mrs Davies had said she'd paid too much for.

From her stand behind the gardenias Julia listened to her colleague's subtle sales talk, and soon the customer, obviously impressed, allowed herself to be escorted to the

26

same mirror shaped like a medallion which had served Julia so well with the young future bridesmaid. The customer, a small brunette, with bright, intelligent eyes and an exquisite hair-do, removed her toque and waited for Betty to fix the delicate gay feathers in her hair.

'See!' exclaimed Betty, standing beside her. 'Madam is superb! This headdress is so soft against a dark skin.'

It was only half a lie. Or perhaps not a lie at all. The customer, Julia decided, looked lovely.

'The feathers are indeed pretty and soft against my hair,' said the customer. 'I am giving a diplomatic reception at the embassy tonight and this headpiece is just what I need to set off my new evening gown. Now that the Paris couturiers are making their evening models longer, something like these small feathers in the hair will become indispensable. How clever of you to be so much in advance of fashion.'

She took a visiting card from her handbag.

'Please have it done up and sent round to the embassy before six.'

Betty was jubilant. Not only had she sold an expensive headpiece but the ambassadress of a small republic had supplied her with the key to her buyer's dilemma. 'With the longer dresses,' she had said, 'these small feathers in the hair will become indispensable.' In these circumstances she might even suggest to Mrs Davies that the price should be carefully reconsidered. Suppose there arose a sudden demand? Women were always happy to pay a little more for what was in advance of fashion.

While Betty was wrapping up her customer's headdress in tissue paper, she used her authority as head of the department to send Julia to tea. 'Twenty minutes,' she said, 'no more, and when you come back it will be my turn.'

Hoping that her tea-break might coincide with Edith's, though it appeared unlikely, Julia darted into the Ladies, scanning the young faces reflected in the long row of mirrors. Naturally enough there was no Edith. Julia slowly washed her hands, then sat down on one of the chairs beside the lockers. Her high-heeled shoes were half a size too small and burnt her feet. All her shoes had always been too small. Every time the door opened she looked up, and from time to time she would glance at the clock. A quarter of an hour later, just as she was about to leave, Edith flew in.

'I thought you might be here,' she said breathlessly. 'I have just had a wonderful piece of luck. The other girls are madly jealous. I managed to sell a customer one of the most expensive dresses in the store. The others tell me that my customer will bring it back tomorrow, but I am certain she will not. She looked so sweet in the dress that her husband will fall in love with her all over again. Have you been waiting long?'

'It doesn't matter,' said Julia, 'and I am glad about the dress.'

'Did you sell anything?'

'Only three gardenias and a bunch of violets, but Betty, the girl in charge of the department, has become quite friendly. That is important, isn't it? I am not as nervous as I was. At all events, thanks for your message. The girl you sent me was rather sweet. Does our arrangement still stand? The first of us to leave after work waits for the other on the pavement in Regent Street?'

'That's it,' said Edith, 'we will walk as far as Piccadilly Circus together.'

The rest of the afternoon passed quickly, and at six o'clock Betty and Julia added up their sales which, together, made a very tolerable total for a Monday.

'I am tired,' said Betty. 'How about you, Julia?'

This was the first time the older girl had addressed her by her Christian name, so that the question, trite in itself, gave such pleasure to Julia that she lost her timidity and asked her companion if she had far to go.

'Unfortunately yes. Quite a way beyond Paddington with at least two changes whether I go by bus or by tube. That's the price I have to pay for continuing to live with my parents. I envy you being in the heart of London. I gather you are virtually home by the time you have walked to Piccadilly Circus?'

'Cambridge Circus,' correct Julia.

'What difference does the length of Shaftesbury Avenue make?' laughed Betty. 'Half a dozen of the West End's most glamorous theatres and the romantic streets of Soho. How I envy you! If I stay at home with my parents it is merely to put money aside so that I can go abroad. Mrs Davies says that if I want to become a buyer it helps a lot to have travelled. She goes from Paris to Rome, from Rome to Madrid, from Madrid to New York and back to London! Isn't it just too romantic? Her husband is a broker in the City. Didn't you find her incredibly smart?'

'Has she any children?'

'No. I suppose one can't have everything.'

Now that the store was closed it was time to put dust sheets over the merchandise so that when the bell rang they were ready to run to the lockers in which they kept their coats and umbrellas.

It was dark by the time Julia, in her coat and little fur cap, emerged into Regent Street crowded with home-going employees from the shops and great stores. Edith was waiting on the opposite pavement and the two girls greeted each other with joyful cries and laughter, linking arms as they tripped off in the direction of Piccadilly Circus. Julia was happy to be with her friend, though she was a little nervous lest the older girl, who appeared to exert so much influence on her, should try to tempt her out of her most direct way home. The picture of her mother waiting after a long, lonely day, haunted her. Nevertheless, the West End was a blaze of movement and gaiety, and she was not insensitive to the romance of Piccadilly Circus shimmering with light and colour. Restaurants, cafés, grill rooms, theatres, bars, pavement news-stands, the slow procession of traffic, the lighted shop windows entranced her. As in Victorian novels, flower sellers sat with their wicker baskets at the base of Eros, wiring sprays and buttonholes for theatre crowds and revellers. A Hollywood film was being shown at the London Pavilion. Youth predominated in the long queue for the next performance—young men with arms round their girls' waists, couples whispering, laughing, heads close together. A boy kissed a girl lightly on her forehead, squeezed her elbow, her hand, said: 'I love you!' The words floated up into the night air. The two girls paused. Their laughter, that had been so carefree and conspiratorial in the store and as they came along Regent Street, died on their young rounded pink lips. Selfconsciously they released each other's linked arms.

'Goodbye!' said Edith, almost savagely. 'I am going to take the tube at Leicester Square. See you tomorrow. Don't forget to bring sandwiches.'

They turned their backs on each other, hurrying off in their different directions, Edith along Coventry Street, Julia down Shaftesbury Avenue.

2

JULIA found her mother tired and petulant with the anxiety of waiting. The moment when Julia would run up the stairs and fly into the room, eager to tell in breathless gasps the details of her fantastic first day at the store, had been looked forward to so impatiently that the worry and the fear she might have been run over in the street had left signs of strain on her mother's normally youthful features. Julia, too exuberant immediately to understand the cause, looked sharply at her mother and noticed for the first time the slight absence of freshness. Was this, she wondered, because she had herself been all day in the store amongst so many girls of her own generation? There had, of course, been Mrs Davies. But Mrs Davies was able to indulge in all the things that Julia's mother could not afford to do, like going regularly to a beautician and having her hair expensively styled. Julia's mother wore her anxious everyday appearance, her end of a dull, uneventful day appearance. Julia suddenly felt ashamed of her own youth and happiness, of the hours in which she had not given so much as a thought to her waiting mother.

The next morning her desire to leave the house was so evident in her eager young features that she could feel the hurt she was inflicting on her mother, but she could not restrain herself. Her mother had reluctantly prepared the sandwiches Julia was to take with her. She had said in a rather grumbling voice that masked her love: 'I don't approve of a girl of your age not having a proper lunch.' Secretly she was also jealous of the enthusiasm Julia had displayed towards her friend Edith, of her talk about how gay and clever Edith was. This aspect of Julia's first day had

31

come as a surprise to her mother, who had spent long hours worrying lest Julia, an inexperienced girl in a new job, might be snubbed or reprimanded. The insidious thought that their mother-daughter relationship of companions and confidantes might soon be shattered in favour of a third person, a younger woman, a stranger, poisoned her happiness.

There was also the fact that Julia, enriched by the acquisition of a new girl-friend nearer to her own age, might stop needing her mother's encouragement and advice. What then would be the use of her? Take away from her the joy of protecting, or on occasion consoling, her child and the future was barren. She felt too young to face such an empty future, such a long stretch devoid of usefulness. Her state of being a woman alone and unprotected, which in simple words was what widowhood amounted to, already appeared harder to bear day by day. Julia with fresh experiences, Julia one stage nearer to marriage, left her with the cold knowledge of what it was like to be a woman in the not so late thirties, the time that was usually of greatest endeavour and fulfilment in a man. Then again, what would happen if Julia were to marry? She could not, would not, impose herself on Julia's husband. Therefore, she would be left alone in this miserable flat behind Charing Cross Road, alone not only by day but also by night. If Julia, on the other hand, were not to marry? That was the worst, the most unthinkable eventuality, the eventuality that smacked of dishonour. Girls, she had been brought up to believe, should always marry young. A bad marriage was better than none.

Julia embraced her mother with great affection, an affection heightened by a tinge of conscience, the sort of heightened affection a husband, about to be unfaithful, might show to his wife.

Lightly and quickly the girl ran down the uncarpeted stairs, slammed the front door behind her (a habit which enraged the woman on the ground floor) and made off down the street to the sound of her high heels hitting the pavement. Because she knew that her mother would be looking down at her from behind one of the flat's curtained windows, Julia was selfconscious. At the corner of the street she saw a girl hurrying ahead of her on the opposite pavement, a girl in a very pretty red coat, a girl who could be none other than Daisy.

Yes, it was Daisy, walking very swiftly, elegant in her red coat and a white silk scarf over her hair.

'Hello,' cried Julia slightly out of breath, having managed to catch up with her without it seeming too obvious that she had been obliged to quicken her step. 'What a piece of luck! I can walk to the store with you and you can show me all the short cuts.'

Julia was proud to be walking with Daisy, who was so much more sophisticated, so elegant and experienced. She must find the right words to express her gratitude to Daisy for having helped her to get her job at the store. 'Yesterday,' she said, 'for my first day I was almost late. I had not realized . . . but today with you, I shall be in plenty of time!'

Daisy did not respond, at least visibly, to Julia's enthusiasm over this chance meeting. She was starting the day in a bad temper, having had a tiff with her family. She had come home late the previous evening and, because her father refused to give her a key, she was obliged to wake up the whole family. This was always happening. When she was a year or two older, perhaps long before that, she would leave home and share a flat with two or three other girls of her own age in a more socially desirable neighbourhood.

As the two girls turned into Poland Street Julia was embarrassed by her companion's ill-contained anger. Her sister Iris, Daisy said, remained at home while she was at work and she was always going through her clothes to borrow a skirt or a jersey. 'I'm sick to death of her!' she exclaimed.

Julia's joy at the new morning gradually lessened. Under Daisy's influence she also fleetingly felt a wind of discontent, though in her case, she told herself vehemently, there was no question of leaving her mother.

They walked quickly, so close to each other that their elbows brushed, their short steps lively, feminine, rhythmic, curiously aware of the lightness and wonder of their extreme youth. Daisy, as her companion supposed, knew all the short cuts. A young man standing in a doorway smiled at her as they passed, calling out a bright good morning.

'Do you know him?' asked Julia, full of admiration.

'Yes, he is the younger Bishop boy. He often takes me dancing. As a matter of fact, though, it is his elder brother, Alan, who chiefly interests me. It was Alan who took me out last night. Oh, it's nothing serious, but I feel relaxed and happy in his company. The parents are tailors, but Alan works in the City. I think he is a bit ashamed of what his parents do. He is ambitious, though too young to support himself. So there is no great hope for me!'

Just before turning into Regent Street the two girls separated. Daisy made her way to the General Office, Julia went to her department to take instructions from Betty.

To her surprise Julia found Betty's expression as unresponsive and withdrawn as on the previous morning. The result was that, sensing trouble, she merely wished her a polite good morning.

'There is a change in plans,' said Betty. 'We are being given a whole new line of accessories, and Mrs Davies is anxious for you to give me a hand in rearranging the department. You can join your friend in Despatch later in the morning.'

'Very well,' said Julia modestly. She put her handbag with Betty's in the drawer and started to flick the sprays of flowers with the feather duster. Betty hummed a popular number from an American musical comedy. This humming, decided Julia, prevented conversation.

Soon, however, moved by a common zeal they began to work harmoniously though silently together. Putting down her duster, Julia carefully arranged the delicate tulle and feather headpieces that Betty handed her from the drawer. The entire store vibrated to the sound of delicate goods being taken out of layers of tissue paper: like the drone of bees under the hot sunshine of electric light in this beautiful gilded cage with its huge glass frontage. Girls from department to department whispered the night's news. 'I told him this. I told him that. We quarrelled. We made it up. We danced till past midnight. He has the most fabulous new car. We had supper overlooking the river at Maidenhead. There were punts with fairy lights and he ordered wine. We came back after midnight and he drove so fast I started to scream.'

Some girls laughed, beautiful silver laughter; others looked sad and disappointed. 'He never phoned and I wore my new dress. I waited all evening and, believe me, nobody rang. I cried.'

Every evening wasted, ill spent, was a defeat in a girl's life. Already before the start of a working day, their minds were totally absorbed in the hope of a new and better experience after the store was closed.

Betty, having unpacked some new feather ornaments, set them up in a pyramid and then stepped back to obtain a painter's perspective of her handiwork. Julia politely offered her opinion that the result was most artistic. 'Alas,' Betty retorted, 'who cares what you think? It is Mrs Davies's opinion I'm worrying about.'

'Maybe,' conceded Julia, 'but I persist in saying that it looks good to me. The fact that you don't attach any importance to what I think has nothing to do with the sureness of my taste.'

Her display of character surprised Betty, and, won over by the implied flattery, she said in a more conciliatory tone:

'Don't misunderstand me. I am very glad to be reassured. It is only that I hardly slept all night. I'm convinced there is a mouse in my room. If only we had a cat—but all the family goes out to work, so there wouldn't be anybody to look after the poor thing until the first of us came home in the evening. Well, that's that. You have been a great help, Julia. You can go down to Despatch now and I'll tell Mrs Davies when she comes that I am very pleased with you. To begin with, it happens to be true, and even if it wasn't, it would be good politics to say so. If I were to tell her you didn't suit, she would send me another girl and I would have to start all over again. So, what's the odds?'

This was not quite what Julia had expected. She would have to learn not to allow her overbrimming enthusiasm, the unrestrained fullness of her heart, to run away with her. Other girls did not necessarily have the same temperament. She must keep the tender part of her character for her mother and for the Prince Charming who was bound to make an appearance soon. With the rest of the world good relations and polite dealing simply must be learnt, in spite of the fact that politeness for politeness's sake did not always come easily to her. Her mother tended to think that polite nothings masked a lie, a deception or, worse still, the weakness of one who fawns. This was perhaps because she had never received much consideration herself. She remained aloof from the world. A great gulf separated the bitter experience of her unhappy marriage and her early widowhood from the lives of the heroines she liked to read about in books. Although aware of the debutantes she read about in the social columns, the models and cover girls whose beauty opened up vast possibilities of wealth and marriage, Julia realistically placed herself in the category of girls for whom life presented a whole series of problems and hurdles. She had no influential father, no powerful friends, no aunt or uncle to leave her a pleasant windfall.

On her way to the stairs she paused to catch the effect of her reflection in a tall mirror. She had the strange feeling that what she had been thinking about had hardened her expression, although it was probably imperceptible to anybody but herself. She tried to smile at herself, but the experiment was a failure, the smile dying on her young lips. My heart is not in it, she told herself. It had not occurred to her that there would ever come a time when this inner ebullience would need to be measured. It had seemed to possess until now an unexpendable quality like the warmth of the sun, the glitter of electric light, the wild hopes of a seventeen-year-old girl.

In the basement Edith was noisily straightening out sheets of crumpled tissue paper and looked furious. When she saw Julia her expression changed to one of relief.

'I was afraid you weren't coming,' she exclaimed, 'and I was furious, furious at the thought that they might have promoted you after just one day in the store. I couldn't bear the idea of another girl being more successful, of you strutting about in the store while I was stuck down in the basement. It's not my fault if I react to everything with violence, but remember—I never forgive an offence!'

'Why should I want to offend you?' asked Julia. 'I had to help Betty unpack a new line and I found her no better tempered than you appear to be. Not only that, I met Daisy on my way to work. Daisy's the girl I told you about who works as a typist in the General Office. She lives almost next door to me, and she was bad tempered too. Her parents refuse to give her a front door key, and she got into trouble for coming home late after going out dancing with a boy she seems vaguely in love with. He's the son of a tailor who is supposed to have quite a nice shop near Poland Street.'

'Oh!' Edith was suddenly interested. 'Personally, after I left you last night I went straight home and found the other girls already in the flat. Seeing that none of us had dates we washed and set one another's hair. One of the girls made such a mess of hers trying to dye it that she had to telephone before going to the office to make a lunch-time appointment with a hairdresser. I myself nearly arrived late at work. I overslept and got very cross while waiting my turn for a bath. We ought to reorganize things but every time we invent a new set of rules, one of us gets boy-friend trouble and the rules are forgotten. Some girls just can't get up in the morning; others stay in bed between jobs and phone boy-friends or wait for boy-friends to phone them.'

She sighed.

'This tissue paper chore breaks a girl's back, but it is supposed to give one pretty shoulders. I never realized the importance of softly rounded shoulders till I began work in the dress department and saw what a difference they can make. A dress hangs better from the moment you slip it on. Would you have thought of that?'

'Where are the two men today?' asked Julia.

'Probably making a spectacle of themselves behind one of the plate glass windows on Regent Street,' said Edith. 'Of the two, I prefer the taller, but it's not that I have the slightest illusion. On my twenty-second birthday I worried a lot about not being married, but now that I have a past——'

'A past? You, a past?' exclaimed Julia, breaking into real laughter for the first time that day. 'What a marvellous idea!'

The tissue paper they were flattening with the palms of their hands made such a noise that they could talk no longer in whispers. Edith repeated that a girl of twenty-two and a bit naturally has something of a past. She conceded that marriage was doubtless the best thing for most girls; it was the only solution, but it depended on the man one came up against. As if throwing out a question, Julia said: 'Perhaps it does not really matter? Being a girl is like being a chameleon. One is adaptable to any environment, to any condition from poverty to wealth. None of us really has much choice. We have to make the best of the unknown. But that doesn't prevent me from dreaming about somebody fabulous. A man who is young, good looking and rich!' She added inconsequently: 'Mother made us ham sandwiches.'

'Then tomorrow,' said Edith, 'I will bring sandwiches with cold tongue.'

'Tongue is expensive,' said Julia.

'I'm not short of money,' said Edith. 'I mean that money is not my problem at the moment. I made quite a lot last month in commission. I have a sort of gift for selling customers the most expensive dresses. It happened again yesterday. You remember? I like working on commission. The salary remains constant but the extra bit fluctuates enough to give one a tingle of excitement. I hate everything that is humdrum. I prefer not to be told in advance the exact sum I shall draw at the end of the week or the end of the month. One of the girls I live with works in the City and she never has time to shop properly. On the other hand, we live in the middle of things, and when I need a dress for myself I can buy whatever I like at quite a big reduction. This girl I was telling you about who works in the City has to do everything in a rush on a Saturday morning. Sometimes she comes to the dress department here and I pretend not to know her. I help her choose something marvellous and then I buy it a few days later as if for myself at a reduced price. We all do it and the only important thing is not to get caught. This girl is rather sweet, but she has a boyfriend who never phones her. She spends half the evening waiting for him to ring, and then ends up by having to phone him herself. There is nothing more damaging to a girl's pride. We all feel as bad about it as she feels herself. Especially as she is extremely pretty. But if she rides on her high horse and refuses to phone, the phone remains silent and the poor girl has a wasted evening. Do you think that is any fun for a girl? A whole evening of her life thrown away reading or washing her hair! Sometimes I wish I were thirty just to know what is going to happen to me, but a moment later the very idea of being thirty terrifies me. What I really want is not to be thirty but to have the experience I will have gathered by then. Meanwhile, there is something else I want—the opportunity to work harder and to live more excitingly. Doing nothing drives me mad. I like selling dresses and collecting my commission at the end of the month. I like going out in the evening with different men. I like guessing what surprises are in store for me. Whether we shall go out to dine, to a dance, to a pub or for a drive in his car. Whether he will kiss me or whether he will not. If a girl fails to have her evenings packed with dates, what is the good of having an evening at all?'

'I never find my evenings too long,' said Julia naïvely. 'Mother and I find plenty to talk about. Besides, she does not allow me to do nothing. She insists that I must knit or sew, that a girl who can do nothing with her hands is like a sham boy. She has taught me to make all my own jumpers and my own dresses.' Julia blushed. 'Mother is a dressmaker professionally. Did I tell you? She is so clever that she is like somebody out of a fairy story. She sews like a spider spinning its web, so delicately that you would need a magnifying glass to see the stitches. I often wonder if there is another woman in all London who can sew more swiftly and more deftly. She is a perfectionist, and when she makes a dress for a customer she takes her work so much to heart that I have seen her weep with suppressed nerves. I've cried myself at seeing her in tears, and when this happens I take her out for a long walk through the streets, perhaps to Soho Square or into one of the parks. She tells me the most surprising stories. She has had enough experience for at least three different lives!'

'It may be all right,' said Edith, 'but it sounds a dull life for you.'

The words died on her lips, for she had seen Daisy walking briskly across the half-empty room. She noticed that Daisy was extremely pretty and shapely in her smart black skirt and the blue jumper that showed off the roundness of her firm young breasts. A natural blonde with a rose-tinted skin, well-shaped legs perched on high heels, Daisy was a picture of secretarial efficiency. Julia, intrigued by Edith's sudden silence and the lifting of her eyes, in turn caught a passing glimpse of Daisy in the half light at the end of the room. Julia had no need to be told that Daisy was attractive to men. Every time they had gone out dancing together, Daisy had been seized upon by an admiring partner almost before they had time to get settled at a table. This was not always the case with Julia who, if Daisy's sister Iris happened to be with them, would remain for a few minutes longer exchanging the sort of talk that girls indulge in selfconsciously while waiting to be chosen by a man. Dancing past them Daisy, clasped in her partner's arms, would wink at her sister and at Julia, amused by their forced animation yet sympathetic and understanding. Julia, who danced well, being light as a feather, conceded that Daisy danced even better than she did. In spite of making all her own dresses, in which she received her mother's expert help, Julia also was obliged to admit that none of her other girl-friends had so many new and becoming dresses as Daisy. The interest Julia now read in Edith's eyes at Daisy's passing filled her with satisfaction. She was more than glad to have such an envied neighbour.

When the brief vision had gone, Julia said meditatively:

'Last night I told Mother all about you. I said you had been very kind to me and that I was fortunate to have you as a friend.'

'You should proceed more cautiously,' laughed Edith. 'I am not nearly so kind as you appear to think. I'm afraid you are going to be disappointed.'

'Why should I be?' said Julia. 'I can't imagine myself trying to harm you.'

'Let us hope we shall remain friends,' said Edith. 'I used to be sentimental and naïve myself at one time. Neither got me anywhere.'

She passed the palm of a hand so roughly over a sheet of tissue paper that it tore. Savagely she screwed it into a tight ball and threw it into a corner of the room.

Even before they were due to go out for lunch, they furtively left their work as they had done the previous day. They washed their hands and made up their faces in the Ladies, quickly swallowed their sandwiches and hurried joyfully out into the sunshine of Regent Street. Passing one of the windows of the great store, Edith exclaimed:

'What did I tell you! There are our two Romeos dressing a nude mannequin in full view of passers-by. At least those young men will know how to clothe their wives when they get married! Let us hope they will prove equally expert in un-dressing them.' She looked at Julia: 'As well as in all the rest.'

Julia blushed, which was just the effect her friend had hoped for. Edith felt a need to show off, to exhibit her superior knowledge in the matter of merchandise. 'As a matter of fact,' she said, 'though I laugh at them, those two young men are gifted. Window dressing is like designing posters and photographing fashion models, one of the modern arts that add lustre to our age. A store like ours, so feminine, so bright and golden, so go-ahead in fashion, takes a tremendous pride in attracting the attention of women who pass in the street. They must be made to believe that our store is different from all the other stores, that they have wandered by some magic spell from London to Paris. Each window is a dream of perfume, shimmering silks and dreams, and a dress on a mannequin must go to the head like a glass of champagne, light and bubbly. Look, for instance, at that little number in front of us in navy blue and white on the platinum-haired mannequin. It's from my department. I'll bet it proves one of the most successful models of the season—whereas the grey number next to it on the dark-haired mannequin, which is also from my department, will prove a flop. Grey is the worst colour. It thickens the waist and makes the wearer look middle aged. So what is it doing there, right in the middle of the window? It is there because the head of our department has fallen in love with it. That is one more reason why I dislike it. When it comes back into stock I'll show it to nobody. I shall leave it at the far end of the department to collect moth. She should have asked my advice, mine and that of the other girls. When I marry that wealthy man who is going to give me a store of my own, I shall sack her and her grey dress. And I'll promote the two window dressers from the basement to the first floor where they will enjoy the light and the fresh air. I shall offer them a fabulous job. Can you see their faces on being offered a job at twice their present salary by me—a girl? It must be wonderful to be a girl with power.'

'Power is not for girls,' said Julia. 'Power is not a feminine desire. I don't dream of being either a millionaire or a newspaper owner—though I believe both exist. I do not want to vote or drive a locomotive. I want to be subjugated and loved.' She added: 'Just now I would like to persuade Mother to invite you for a meal at home. I'm longing for her to meet you, and for you to meet her.'

No sooner had she said this than Julia thought:

'Edith really is astoundingly clever, but I must be careful not to hurt Mother's feelings by singing her praises. I must find a more subtle way of bringing them together.'

The two girls pursued their rather aimless walk in the direction of Oxford Circus, but neither spoke, and it was as if a wall of silence had sprung up between them. Neither had any idea what the other was thinking, but both appeared troubled.

Back at the store Julia was no longer afraid to be left alone in the department during Betty's lunch hour. Now that Monday was past, business had quickened and she no longer had time even for the shortest chat with the cashier in the gilded cage. The influx of young secretaries and typists not only from the West End but from the City was considerable, and because they were in a hurry and uncertain of themselves, Julia found them easy to influence. A sprig of flowers, a hair ornament, a few gay coloured feathers, a bangle are not expensive accessories. They are not likely to ruin a girl, though any purchase needs careful thought. The different youthful, puzzled and animated expressions delighted Julia who gained confidence at every new sale. Behind her table she felt like the manipulator of a puppet show. Excitement coursed in her veins. She revelled in the responsibility.

A middle-aged woman, looking nervously round, finally asked in an embarrassed whisper if Miss Betty was still in the department. She then made as if to go, turned back and said: 'I should have guessed that she would be at lunch at this time. Have you replaced the girl who left to get married?'

'Yes,' answered Julia. 'Betty told me yesterday that she is married and has gone to Canada. It sounded terribly romantic.'

'Perhaps not so romantic as you think,' said the woman with the tired, drawn features. 'I happen to be the girl's

43

mother, and I came to ask Betty if she had any news of her. I've not heard from her since she left and I am utterly miserable. So miserable, my dear, that I can neither eat nor sleep, and there are moments when I feel that I am going mad.'

She asked wildly: 'Has Betty heard from her? Do you happen to know? They seemed to be quite good friends. Sometimes there are confidences between girls of the same age that are not there between daughter and mother, though you just can't imagine how close I was to my daughter. We were more like sisters.'

Julia felt the blood rushing to the roots of her hair. It might almost have been her own mother talking. The thought that her own daughter-mother relationship might one day suffer such unbearable strain appalled her. She heard the woman ask distractedly for the second time: 'Has Betty heard from her? Do you happen to know?'

'She did not give me that impression,' said Julia. 'I think she was even a little hurt that your daughter had not invited her to the wedding. But I am new here. I only arrived yesterday. There was no reason for Betty to have told me anything. Do please sit down. She is due back at any moment.'

Leaving the girl's mother in order to serve a customer, Julia found her earlier happiness clouded. The woman looked timidly round the department which must have changed hardly at all since her daughter had worked there. As soon as Julia was able to rejoin her, she said pitifully:

'I should not have come. I feel worse looking at everything. I keep hoping that I shall see Janet appearing from behind a cluster of those artificial flowers. I can't believe that she's not here still, that she really got married and went to Canada. But no, she is not here. You have replaced her, and one day Betty will go, and the other girls who remember her will change their jobs and get married and there will be nobody left I can talk to.'

'There is Betty!' exclaimed Julia.

'Hello!' said Betty breezily as she put her handbag into its accustomed place in the drawer. 'What news of Janet?'

44

'None,' said the woman in a broken voice. 'I came to see if you had any.'

The anxiety in her tone struck Betty who looked up sharply. She answered almost tenderly:

'Janet never wrote to any of us after she left the store. We had hoped to be invited to the wedding. Some of us who had known her better than the others were rather disappointed. Oh, and jealous too, I expect. Those of us who are still waiting for husbands, I mean. But in a way she was probably right. When a girl starts a new life, she does not want to force her former girl-friends on a young, impetuous husband. He has married her, not all the other girls in the store. As a matter of fact, I've been planning for weeks to call on you. Janet left her beige cardigan here. I put it in tissue paper and hid it safely at the back of this drawer.'

She slowly withdrew the small package and held it out.

'Oh, no!' murmured the woman. 'It is as if she were dead and you were handing me all that was left of her personal possessions. I can't stand it.'

'Nonsense!' exclaimed Betty. 'It can't be as bad as all that. Probably Janet is too happy to write.'

'I have no address for her,' said the woman, 'and it is nine weeks.'

Betty looked round anxiously. She feared a scene in front of potential customers.

'Julia,' she whispered. 'Would it not be rather nice if you saw Janet's mother to the door?'

'Of course,' said Julia, warm-heartedly.

On Julia's return, Betty was taking advantage of a temporary lull to pack the day's mail orders and get them ready for the post. As head of her department it was her duty to deal with postal requests for a sprig of flowers, a necklace, a belt, a delicate head-spray. The goods would be wrapped carefully in tissue paper, placed in a cardboard box, tied up in brown paper and labelled. Soon, together with scores of other parcels of every shape and size, they would

45

be taken by the little old man in his osier basket to Despatch in time to catch the country mail.

'You know,' said Betty, writing the last label, 'one can never be quite sure of mail orders. Mostly they are based on highly decorative drawings in the current catalogue. A customer dreams up her own version of the article and if it does not conform to her imagination, she promptly sends it back.'

'I know,' said Julia. 'The palms of my hands are sore from straightening out the tissue paper from rejected dresses. Edith, the other girl, told me all about it.'

'Yes, but there is more good than bad. Besides, for what we do sell by post we get the same commission as if we had sold it over the counter. If you make good here you will no doubt get your share.'

Mrs Davies, who had not yet made her appearance, now arrived smoothly, lightly, bringing with her an aura of delicious French perfume. Greeting the two girls she wished them a polite, rather distant good-day. 'There's a woman,' thought Julia, 'who must be at her ease at every level of society.' Her navy blue dress was obviously an original model from a world-famous *couture* house, and her hair-do once again excited Julia's admiration. Was it possible that she went to the hairdresser every day? Her long, well-shaped legs and her extremely smart shoes produced looks of admiration and envy from passing customers, and Julia felt that Mrs Davies must be the sort of woman to value other women's admiration, the most valuable of all for a woman to obtain.

After a murmured conversation with Betty about new merchandise, the day's mail orders and plans for the next day, Mrs Davies raised her voice:

'Next week if we continue to be pleased with our new assistant it would be nice to let her handle some of the mail orders. That was your policy with Janet, wasn't it?'

'Yes, madam,' said Betty selfconsciously. She treated Mrs Davies with immense respect.

'I take it that you have already shown her how the

46

parcels are made up? A department can only prove a real success if the girls who run it work in perfect harmony.'

Turning to Julia, she said:

'I would not like you to stay in a department where you were not perfectly happy or where you did not consider yourself indispensable.'

'But I love it!' exclaimed Julia. 'Everything is so pretty. It is like working in a garden.'

'I am glad,' said Mrs Davies. Then turning to Betty:

'I think we also are fortunate to have Julia, don't you?'

She allowed the words to hover a moment over the coronets and feathers. Then she asked:

'Have we any news of Janet?'

'No, Madam,' answered Betty. 'Nor has her mother who came to see us here after lunch in case we might know something. She was very upset.'

'These things happen,' said Mrs Davies. 'She was obviously a very possessive mother and now she must feel intolerably lonely. I feel really sorry for her, but I think Janet needed to feel the power of her own wings. She always gave me the impression of having been rather too subdued by her mother. A girl needs to have a personality of her own. Perhaps if she ever comes back to pay us a visit, she will surprise us.'

Turning again to Julia, she said:

'Do you live in the suburbs?'

'Oh, no, Madam, only a few minutes away, in Soho, but as there is no direct bus it is easier to walk.'

'Well, as long as it does not rain,' said Mrs Davies. 'Otherwise it can be hard on your clothes. I like your little black dress. It suits you admirably and sets off your golden hair. Home made, I suppose?'

'Mother and I made it together, or I should say that Mother made it almost entirely.'

'Your mother must be a clever woman. Home-made clothes need to be expertly cut to compete against the ready-made market, but just once in a while, as in your case, there is the exception. There can be a fortune in deft fingers and if

47

you sew yourself it will help you to get on in a store like his one. Well, goodbye, Betty. Goodbye, Julia.'

Mrs Davies left them with a smile, leaving behind her the impression of being a woman loved, a woman sure of herself, a woman with an important husband who could make life comfortable for her and who saw to it that she had affection in the home. These were the things that gave her this immense assurance. Added together, they constituted that almost complete happiness that most women dream about. When she had gone Betty murmured with slightly pinched lips:

'You appear to have made quite a hit with our buyer!'

'I have not been here a week yet,' said Julia. 'There is still plenty of time for me to displease her.'

But Betty was looking with absorption at her dress.

'I must admit,' she said, 'that Mrs Davies was right about that black dress. Though I'm not sure why, it does have something special. Until she noticed it I had never given it a thought. Frankly, you did rather get on my nerves with your golden hair and terrible *joie de vivre*. I never met a girl so starry-eyed. What on earth is there to be so happy about? As for your dress, there is no particular reason why I should have noticed it. I can't sew and when I have to do the simplest thing like sewing on a button, I'm all thumbs. I don't even own a thimble. I can knit after a fashion, though I seldom finish what I start. Sitting still, arms pressed to my side, legs primly together, eternally passing a needle through the same loop bores me stiff. I can't believe we were put into the world to do that. I don't even like staying indoors, as so many girls do, tidying a cupboard, ironing a dress, polishing a table. I get a great urge to be out and about. Selling things, any sort of thing, gives me an important, vital feeling. It gives me the excitement, in however limited a way, of making money. The women on my mother's side nearly all have small shops, dress shops, hat shops, haberdashery, but my father is not capable of running anything and while my mother was bringing us children up he managed to land us on the rocks. Every time my parents quarrel and have a blazing row, the story of the shop comes

48

up, how if it had not been for his incompetence we should still own it. Now he works as a traveller for a firm in Hanover Square, and mother stays at home hating it. Occasionally we have lodgers. All that of course makes life very dreary for me.'

After work, Edith was the first of the two friends to leave the store and, as on the previous night, she stood waiting for Julia in the effervescence of Regent Street. This time, however, she was on edge. She had not sold a single dress. There were days like that. She now had something more pressing on her mind. The boy-friend who was vaguely supposed to be taking her out that night had given no sign of life and she was desperately anxious therefore to get home as quickly as possible in case he should telephone.

'Don't let us go to Piccadilly Circus tonight,' she said, putting her arm through Julia's and leading her in the opposite direction. 'Walk with me as far as Oxford Circus and while I dive down into the Underground you can walk home by way of Poland Street.'

'I do hope he telephones,' said Julia sympathetically.

'How can I even decide what to wear,' said Edith, 'until I know what he has in mind?'

They parted in Argyll Street in front of the Palladium, where there was always a great crowd of people queuing up for the next performance, jostling around the brightly lit booking office, examining the photographs of artistes hanging outside the main entrance, and surging round the fruit barrows with their acetylene lamps beside the tube station.

This was the London Julia loved best. She walked on to Oxford Street and wove her way with quick, happy steps through the crowds, stopping to look at a dress in a dress shop, shoes in a shoe shop, pausing again to see what foreign film, French or German, they were showing at the Academy cinema. Then she turned into Poland Street with its small tailors and music publishers, and turned again to cross Berwick Street and Wardour Street, home of the

49

motion picture industry, and went through Carlisle Street with its glittering new cafés into Soho Square.

The quiet gardens in the centre of the square, with green lawns and shady trees, made a little pool of darkness in the midst of a city of light whose reflection reddened the night sky. Charing Cross Road and Oxford Street, at right angles to each other, sent up a muted roar of distant traffic. Here was peace. Here were an Irish Catholic church, a French Protestant church, a silent jam factory, an old people's home. Leaving the square by Greek Street, Julia walked past French, Greek and Italian restaurants, some garlanded with Chinese lanterns, all exhaling the smell of foreign food, garlic and olive oil. Bottles of Chianti hung on string. Some restaurants had small tables overflowing on to the pavement, with red lamps on the white tablecloths and shining silver and green bushes in tubs all round. A foreign-looking waiter with an apron round his waist seemed ready to spring to attention at the sight of a potential customer. Music could be heard. Coloured maps of Adriatic resorts and Greek islands tempted the passer-by. Small shops of foreign food, night clubs in basements, girls standing in dark alleyways—then the end of Old Compton Street with its newsagents who sold foreign newspapers, from Rome, from Madrid, from Paris.

At the corner of Julia's street, dark and mysterious after the brilliant foyer of the Palace Theatre where patrons in evening dress were already arriving in cars that had come round Cambridge Circus, she saw suddenly two figures clasped together against the railings of a house. The girl, perched on her high heels, had her young face turned up lovingly to the man who slowly bent down to kiss her. The girl wore a very pretty red coat. It was Daisy.

Julia paused a moment, moved as she might have been by a tender love scene in a play, then she hurried across to the opposite pavement, not to embarrass them and not to be seen. She slipped the key into her front door and ran quickly, lightly up the stairs. There were voices from the living-room. Her mother was talking to another woman, probably a client trying on a new dress. Business girls often came for fittings on their way home from work. Anxious not to disturb them, Julia crept silently into the adjoining small room where her mother kept half-finished dresses which hung side by side in a curtained-off alcove. This room, which contained a rather pretty bed, was supposed to be Julia's, but more often than not she would decide, after a long evening of reading or gossip with her mother, to spend the night on a couch by the window in her mother's room. When she was with her mother, she feared none of the things that so often kept her awake or gave her bad dreams, such as death, which was very real to her because she was a slim delicate little thing, or poverty which always haunted her because of her mother's constant fear of it. She was also afraid, now that she was so happy at the store, to be sent away from it. There was, too, the ever-present fear that the right Prince Charming might not make his appearance, though on this score she put a good deal of faith in her unbounded vitality. However, it was no good pretending that the future did not torment her.

She now heard her mother calling: 'Come in, Julia!' And when she went into the living-room she recognized one of her mother's customers who worked with a famous West End catering firm whose hand-made chocolates and wedding cakes had graced the homes of the English aristocracy for several generations. Miss Pauline, delighted with the dress that Julia's mother was making for her, smiled affectionately at Julia and asked whether she was happy at the store. Miss Pauline had brought her a large box of chocolates that she had filled herself from the little back room in the main shop where hundreds of freshly made chocolates were ranged on specially made shelves so that a customer could choose the kinds he liked best, the box being filled before his eyes before being tied up in pink or blue ribbon. During a lengthy fitting Miss Pauline had already told most of her news to Julia's mother, but now she told it all over again to Julia, and it seemed as if she would never go. As this was not like her, Julia and her mother exchanged glances of surprise. After what seemed an interminable time, however, the front door bell rang and Miss Pauline jumped up and exclaimed, rather red in the face: 'That must be for me. I told my gentleman friend he could meet me here! He is taking me out to dinner and a show!'

As Miss Pauline gathered up her things, Julia thought of Edith hurrying home not to miss her boy-friend's telephone call, of Daisy being kissed by a young man in the street, of Miss Pauline being taken to dinner and a show by a gentleman friend and suddenly her own evening, those hours normally so tenderly appreciated, seemed by contrast less desirable and too empty of romance.

The next morning, while Julia was finishing breakfast, she listened for the opening and closing of Daisy's front door down the street. This was a sound that she had learnt to distinguish over a period of time. Though she was short-sighted, she made up for it by an acute sense of hearing, and and this was both a delight to herself and a surprise to her friends. Daisy's front door, as she left for work, would be slammed shut with such a noise that no other front door on the street could equal it, and then along the pavement would be heard the quick, short steps of Daisy as she sped along on high heels.

This morning Julia longed to accompany Daisy through the labyrinth of streets. The moment she heard Daisy's front door she would take up her gloves and handbag and kiss her mother goodbye. Then she would fly down the stairs just in time to find herself face to face with her friend. She would tell Daisy about her second day in the store, repeat her gratitude for Daisy's part in getting her the job and then reveal tactfully, knowingly, that she had seen her the previous evening being kissed by a boy-friend, and that she hoped they had spent a beautiful, romantic evening together.

The minute hand of her mother's alarm clock was advancing dangerously, and if Julia did not leave the house now she would be late. She swallowed her coffee, kissed her mother, took up her handbag and gloves and hurried down the stairs hoping that even at this late hour she might catch sight of Daisy. She was disappointed. Looking up to wave a final goodbye to her mother at the window she quickened her steps, wondering if perhaps her friend might already be crossing Cambridge Circus. But there was no sign of Daisy.

In the end Julia arrived out of breath and rather too early at the store. She went straight to the Ladies, washed her hands, combed her hair and took advantage of the excellent light to make up her lips and eyes. Her haste in chasing after the elusive Daisy, and the fact that the morning was already too warm to wear the coat her mother had insisted she must still wear, had made her feel hot and uncomfortable. Now she had regained confidence. Her small red lips and golden hair gave her an appealing childlike appearance.

Having been instructed by Betty the previous day to do so, Julia went straight to Despatch. Edith had not yet arrived, but the younger of the two window dressers, looking distant and pensive, sat on the edge of the table he normally shared with his companion. His long legs were gently swinging. Though he intimidated Julia, she gave him such a long, interested look as she passed him that it woke him out of his day-dream and he said:

'Good morning, Blondie. What have you done with your girl-friend?'

'She'll be along,' said Julia. 'Is your companion late too?'

'He has a hobby,' said the young man, 'a second string to his bow. He buys second-hand cars that nobody wants, tinkers with them and sells them at a profit to his friends. He has probably had a break-down on the Great North Road.'

'You mean he makes a habit of it?'

'He takes calculated risks. Being ambitious he tries to make money in two ways, dressing mannequins in shop windows and re-selling motor cars. He appears determined to make a small fortune before he is twenty-five.'

'Are you like that too?'

'No,' said the young man. 'I don't think so, but that doesn't prevent me from being ambitious.'

The girl in the orange jumper and tweed skirt whom Julia had met on her first day came in from the General

Office with files and correspondence. She put them on Julia's table.

'These are for you,' she said. Then turning to the young man she said: 'Has your friend Christopher had another break-down?'

Julia longed to ask her if Daisy had arrived yet, but she lacked the courage to do so. The girls who worked in the General Office intimidated her.

Christopher and Edith, for no other reason than that the clock happened to be striking the hour, arrived together. Julia, looking up from the file she had opened more to pretend she was busy than to study it, wondered if perhaps her friend had taken advantage of this meeting to flirt a little with Christopher. But this did not appear to have been the case. In spite of the many successes she claimed to have enjoyed with men in the past Edith remained shy and reserved with these two. Without exchanging a word she and Christopher went straight to the tables where their partners waited for them. Julia was mildly surprised that, though they were surrounded by so many pretty girls, the men in this great store appeared much to prefer their own company during the lunch and tea breaks so that the girls were left strictly to themselves.

As soon as Edith had settled down Julia asked eagerly: 'What happened last night? Did he telephone?'

'No,' said Edith disgustedly, 'he did not. The hours I have wasted waiting for the telephone to ring! Not that this particular one was really worth waiting for. But three girls in the same flat watch one another like cats. What is worst about a broken date is the humiliation of it. That, and one more evening wasted. Every time I meet a man I convince myself that he is the one and only I have been waiting for all my life, so I stand on tiptoe to hang a halo over his head. I get blinded by the brilliance of his imagined qualities and then I usually discover that he is already married, is just out of jail, is a bankrupt or has a mistress in Peckham Rye. What did you do last night?'

'I? Oh, nothing. Mother had a dress to finish. Her

54

customer came late for her fitting and she wasted so much of our time waiting for a gentleman friend to call for her that by the time we had finished supper it was too late even to go to the cinema. You know, Edith, what worries me is what Mother will do all by herself in the evening if ever I have a boy-friend. I am almost glad that it has not happened to me yet. Do you find me very peculiar?'

Edith laughed.

'Having a boy-friend is nothing,' she said, 'as long as there are no complications.'

'What do you mean by complications?'

Edith glanced at her companion, wondering if she was as naïve in matters of sex as she was in certain other respects. On further consideration she thought not. A mother-daughter relationship of the kind practised by Julia and her mother would preclude too many secrets. Perhaps Julia was a prude or had not wanted to read into Edith's remark an intended suggestion of personal experience.

'Am I as disillusioned today as I was trying to suggest?' wondered Edith. 'At all events my innuendo misfired.' A more satisfactory explanation of her bad temper could wait.

Meanwhile Julia with that butterfly mind of hers was already thinking about something quite different. She murmured out of the blue:

'I expect Christopher is clever enough and I'd like him to make a fortune before he's twenty-five, but I personally prefer the younger one.'

'How do you know that the elder one is called Christopher?' asked Edith, suddenly alert. 'Who told you his name?'

'The girl from the General Office, the one in the orange jumper and the tweed skirt. She called him that.'

'You certainly know a lot of things,' said Edith. 'Undoubtedly these two boys have a higher opinion of the girls from the General Office than they have of us. Of me, for instance. Provincial girls, like me, who live with other girls in a shared London flat strike me as being at a disadvantage compared with girls who live with their parents.'

Pursuing her train of despondency, she said:

'One of the girls who live with me is in love with her employer, a Harley Street specialist, a man with grown children. From Monday till Thursday her life is full of hope. On Friday he goes to his family in the country and she takes a sleeping pill or runs off to consult a fortune teller.'

'She may end by marrying him,' said Julia. 'The newspapers are full of strange happenings. Stranger things than a girl marrying a Harley Street specialist with grown-up children. In fact lots of girls in real life do far more exciting things than the heroines in most novels. As for you, I envy all that experience you must have had. I am still waiting for my first boy-friend.'

She looked thoughtfully at Edith who, in spite of the little lines of bitterness round her mouth, was such a beautiful girl. In fact her dark beauty radiated like a tropical sun, and Julia simply could not fathom how any young man who had a chance of spending an evening with Edith should have failed to telephone her. What more exciting thing could possibly happen to him than going out with this radiant girl? This was a thing about men that Julia was not yet able to understand, that so many appeared blind to the pretty girls round them.

Though Julia and Edith met, as usual, after work some of the excitement had worn off. They turned automatically, as on the first evening, in the direction of Piccadilly Circus, and after a while they were joined by Betty who came running after them. Edith and Betty, by common consent, decided to go dancing, and though they invited Julia to come with them, she felt that it would not be fair on her mother who would be waiting anxiously for her return, probably with some dish carefully and lovingly prepared.

Betty, who had met Edith only once or twice quite by accident in the Ladies, was obviously delighted by this new friendship, a fact which, quite apart from being robbed by her conscience of an evening's fun, cast a cloud over Julia's usual high spirits. She knew that the moment her back was turned the two older girls would begin tearing her to pieces. She should not have placed Edith in a category apart, the category of special friend. Julia decided that one of her chief faults was a lack of moderation in almost everything she did, especially when her affections were in question. Her mother had warned her on several occasions about this. It was difficult learning to become a woman. Life was full of pitfalls. At one moment one was told to curb one's secret emotions, the next that a girl's success depended on her spontaneity. Her mother even claimed that girls with overflowing spirits, who carried their own sunshine about them like luxuriantly exotic flowers, found a rich husband much more quickly than those cold, static cover girls who, with their unsmiling profiles and exactly right hip and bust measurements, too often intimidated men. 'But on the whole,' thought Julia, waving farewell to her companions in Leicester Square outside the dance hall, 'chance must be the main factor. Otherwise, why do so many girls, even in this ultra-scientific age, still consult fortune tellers? Why does Betty buy a newspaper on her way to work only for the horoscope it contains? Why did the head of the stocking department, an astute, clever girl, and one of the youngest department heads in the store, come over to ask me during the tea break if it was true that I had a gift for reading a person's future in a pack of playing cards?'

Having come up Charing Cross Road, Julia turned from Cambridge Circus into her street and saw Daisy's mother standing in the half-open door of her house. She was a stout woman with prematurely white hair and legs swollen with housework. The long coral earrings studded with glass diamonds that hung from her lobes made her appear even more rotund. Julia was about to wish her good evening and ask about Daisy when, swiftly and silently, the rotund figure withdrew inside her house and closed the door. Julia wondered what she had done so clearly to annoy her neighbour. Interpreting the incident as a slight, the blood rushed to the roots of her hair and she was so upset that it was the first thing she told her mother on entering the flat.

'I'm sure you misjudge her,' Julia's mother said. 'She has no reason to insult you!'

But all the same, moving cautiously to the window, she drew the net curtain aside and looked down into the street.

'How curious!' she exclaimed. 'Daisy's mother is back on her doorstep, and it looks to me as if she were waiting for somebody—perhaps for Daisy. That might well explain the reason for her not wishing to speak to you.'

'I hoped you might come to see me at the store this afternoon,' said Julia. 'You half promised.'

'I had a terrible accident,' she said, looking suddenly tired. 'My iron was too hot and I scorched part of the hem of a dress. Fortunately I had just enough material left over to cut a new section for the bias skirt. I ought to have guessed. I read my fortune in the cards after you went to work and there was nothing but spades. I have had a black Wednesday. That reminds me. There is this letter for you by the afternoon mail.'

Julia tore the envelope open, and having read the contents exclaimed: 'Look! It's an invitation to a wedding! From the daughter of the little man who owned the draper's shop in Berwick Street where I worked a few weeks before going to the store. Alice! That was her name! I am surprised she has invited me. She was not particularly friendly when I worked with her. I wonder now that she is getting married whether she will leave the shop? At all events I shall not go. I can't afford a new dress and new shoes just to go to Miss Alice's wedding. But you were wrong about it being black Wednesday. We ought to call it Surprise Wednesday what with Daisy's mother slamming her front door in my face, you burning a dress and then making it as new again and now this amazing invitation to a wedding. How old do you suppose Alice can be? I bet she is every day of thirty!'

Julia sighed. While washing up the supper things, she sang an American dance tune that made her think with a tinge of jealousy about Betty and Edith out dancing. Tomorrow they would tell her all about it. She wiped her hands on the towel above the gas cooker and took out of her mother's wardrobe a cardboard box in which she kept her personal treasures—various gloves, a garland of flowers from a spring hat, a gold lamé evening bag, some lace and ribbons. But all these things, since her eyes had become accustomed to the shining brightness of the pretty goods in the Regent Street store, appeared slightly tarnished. How wonderful it would be to start again from zero. Yet at the same time she knew that it would be impossible to part with objects, however faded, that had been gifts from mother to daughter. She turned her mind to Mrs Davies. How elegant she was with her pearl necklace and her hand-made shoes. Italian, she supposed. She undressed, vigorously brushed her hair a hundred times, proud of its golden supple-ness, and slipped into her white silk nightdress. It was too long for her, falling to her feet and allowing her to pretend for a moment that it was a wedding gown. Alice's invitation to the wedding still lay on the table where her mother had put it. At the thought that Alice had a whole draper's shop from which to choose her trousseau, she who was every day of thirty and not very pretty at that, Julia whispered: 'I shall not go, I shall not go.' She took the gold-rimmed card and tore it into several pieces. Then she opened the window and flung them out so that they fluttered on to the empty milk bottles ranged before the front door. The night was clear and beautiful and the sky full of stars. She would refuse to wear that hot winter coat tomorrow.

She walked to work thoughtfully but briskly, enjoying the sunshine and the busy scene about her. These narrow streets were full of unexpected glimpses of domestic tranquillity or drama. Without having consciously set out to do so she had taken the same route along which she and Daisy had walked the morning they met the young Bishop whose parents were tailors near Poland Street and with whose brother Daisy had gone dancing the night she came home late and had angry words with her family. At the corner of the same street Julia once again came upon the younger of the two boys. She had, in fact, only a few seconds earlier passed his parents' shop and had tried to glance inside, but because of the frosted glass, on which the family name was painted, she had seen nothing but some rolls of worsted.

Taken by surprise at this chance meeting the young man did not dare run after her or call out, and Julia, for her part, was much too nervous and shy to look back. Instead, moved by a feeling of false pride or dignity, she hastened her step. This she regretted later, but after all was it not for the man to take the initiative in such circumstances?

Today Julia went first to Artificial Flowers and, as Betty had not yet arrived, she started to take down the tissue paper and light cotton dust sheets that the girls placed on the stands before going home at night. The cashier in her golden cage was putting rose-tinted varnish on her nails, and the head of the stocking department, who was still being very polite to Julia in the hope that she might tell her fortune in the cards, came over to bid her good morning. Julia was beginning to feel very much at home in this light and colourful feminine store where the different departments were dotted about like carefully tended beds of flowers in one large *parterre*.

Betty arrived with quick happy steps, looking prettier than Julia had ever seen her. She even thanked Julia with a smile for having taken the dust sheets off the stands.

'Yes,' she said, 'we had a wonderful time at the dance hall and we were asked for almost every dance. Different young men all the evening except towards the end when two boys invited us to the cafeteria for ices and then escorted us to Leicester Square tube station. They both work in the same bank, and as they go dancing every Wednesday we've made a date with them for next week.'

'How did you get on with Edith?'

'She is a beautiful dancer, light as a butterfly, and although she kept very sweet to me she was much bolder than I am with men. Oh, I was forgetting. In the Ladies we met a girl from the General Office you apparently both know.'

'Daisy?' asked Julia excitedly.

'No, that was not her name. She was wearing an orange jumper and a tweed skirt and had come with her boy-friend, who owns a scooter.'

Disappointed, Julia said:

'I'd better run or I'll be late.'

Edith was, in fact, waiting for her at their table in the basement. Julia, her face shining, exclaimed: 'Betty tells me that you had a wonderful time last night!'

'Not bad,' said Edith. 'Amusing but a wasted evening all the same. Nothing important or permanent will come of it.'

'How did you get on with Betty?'

'I liked her very much. By the way, we met the girl from the General Office who brings us the files every morning. I misjudged her. She is not nearly as superior as I thought at first. She was quite sweet last night.'

While they were talking the girl in question arrived to deposit her load on their table. This morning she greeted them with such a friendly smile that Julia decided to ask her point blank the question that had been troubling her for the last twenty-four hours.

'Has Daisy been promoted?' she asked. 'I have not seen her around.'

The girl's expression turned to one of surprise and suspicion.

'Has nobody told you?' she asked. 'Daisy is not here any more.'

She paused, apparently trying to satisfy herself about the reason for Julia's question. Then she said:

'Why do you ask? Did you know her?'

'We live in the same street—well, practically next door to each other. I have been madly worried and last night her mother slammed the front door in my face just as I was going to speak to her.'

As the girl in the orange jumper did not answer, Julia persisted:

'Is she ill? Do please tell me.'

'No,' said the girl. 'She is not ill. It was not because of illness that she left.'

'Then I simply don't understand!' cried Julia.

But the girl from the General Office had said as much as she dared for the moment, and turning sharply on her high heels she made her way back across the half-empty room.

Alone with Edith, Julia decided out of loyalty to her neighbour not to pursue the questions that were in her mind. Instead she said:

'The girl whose father owns the draper's shop where I worked for a short time before I came here is to be married. She sent me an invitation to her wedding, but I have decided not to go.'

'Then you are wrong,' said Edith. 'A girl should never refuse an invitation to a wedding. She never knows whom she might meet. Men who go to weddings are liable to catch the marrying fever, the desire to do likewise that is as infectious as measles at weddings. Though in my own case the romance that began at a wedding did not end a bit well.'

'Tell me!' urged Julia, sensing that this was going to prove the key to her friend's past. 'Tell me!'

'I was to be the chief bridesmaid, and I was deliriously happy. I had a lovely dress and everything I wore that day was as new as the clothes the bride herself was to wear. This heady sensation of being dressed from head to feet in new clothes is something I've never been able to recapture. It did not spring from pride or extravagance, as it might have if somebody had handed me a million, but from something, oh, so much more wonderful and important—the feeling that I had suddenly and magically become a woman. Everything that had happened to me until then seemed trivial. My cupboards, full of schoolgirl clothes, stood wide open. I tumbled everything out on the floor and in a sweeping gesture I gave them all to my young sister. Yes, everything! My mother, who seemed as young and laughing as myself, helped me put on my bridesmaid's dress and went with me to the wedding.

'What a wonderful, wonderful day! My mother was so happy that anyone would have thought she was marrying her daughter off to the most eligible young man in the town instead of merely watching her be a bridesmaid. We were not particularly rich, and she must have spent a good deal more than she could afford buying me all those clothes. The bride was the daughter of one of her school friends and my mother was so touched and proud that I had been picked to be a bridesmaid. She wanted me to be the prettiest and the most carefully turned out.'

Edith appeared to lose herself a little at this point in her story. She began feverishly to write names and addresses of customers on catalogue envelopes, and Julia pretended to do the same. At what point would Edith take up the tale again? Would her confessions come out like a muddled skein of wool?

'We returned from the wedding with a great many new clothes that Mother and I bought in the town's stores. It was a May wedding and some people claim that May weddings are unlucky for the bride. The bride, as far as I know, has been happy ever since. But as far as I'm concerned, her bridesmaid, there could not have been a more unfortunate wedding, and it would take more than a miserable evening's dancing with your friend Betty in Leicester Square to make me forget it. It would need a whole lot more than that, nothing less than some huge, devastating vengeance on life itself, and though I dislike saying it, my parents were the ones who made me suffer most in this whole terrible affair.'

She had laid down her pen and was clutching at her throat as if in physical pain. Julia, watching this development, was embarrassed. Yet Julia was accustomed, through her mother and her mother's many clients, to hearing feminine confidences. Many women who came to her mother for a fitting no sooner started to undress than they began to pour out all their secrets. Edith's affliction was painful to watch. Julia wanted to clap her hands to her ears. She was frightened in the way she was occasionally frightened by the size and power of those red London buses which made her feel they wanted to run her over. She felt so slight beside their huge majesty. Edith's outburst disappointed her. She had looked forward to a gay account of the two girls' adventures at the dance. Her mind was not prepared for tragedy.

Pulling herself together Edith suddenly said:

'By the way, last night at the dance hall I discovered his Christian name.'

'Whose name?' asked Julia, wondering whom her friend was talking about.

'The boy who works with Christopher,' Edith explained in a whisper. 'The girl from the General Office told me when I met her in the Ladies. Are you not longing to know?'

'Actually I met him on the stairs on my way down to join you. He called out "Hello!"'

'His name is Francis!'

She laughed illogically. Her face had suddenly become so full of fun that Julia could hardly believe it was the same girl. The little man from Despatch who wheeled his osier basket from one department to the other, collecting parcels for the mail, arrived this time with a new load of empty white cardboard boxes and crumpled tissue paper. He said:

'The things you girls find to laugh about! Like a lot of chirping sparrows, and I bet there is not an intelligent thought in either of your frivolous heads. Goodness me! Girls are all the same!'

'That's all right,' said Edith sweetly. 'Just tip everything on to the floor. We are busy addressing envelopes.'

'Very well, miss,' he said politely. 'Maybe, if you've no objection, I will just stay long enough to have a smoke.'

He smelt of stale smoke and the balsam he rubbed in for his rheumatics. As soon as he had gone off into a corner of the room, Edith began to itemize the exceptional expenditure of her week, a coat she had sent to the cleaners and a pair of shoes to be re-heeled. She wondered if either of the girls she shared the apartment with would remain in

London over the weekend or if she would be the only one. If the latter were to prove the case, she would spring clean the whole place, and perhaps, if she were lucky, some boy-friend might telephone.

Because it was raining and both girls felt a sudden void in their hearts, they went to an Italian café for lunch. Secretly Julia would have preferred to be alone, but she did not dare say this to her friend, though for all she knew Edith might be thinking the same. Julia had almost decided to rush home and surprise her mother, who had looked pale after a disturbed night during which she had worried, as she increasingly did worry, about the dresses she made for difficult women. If a Prince Charming did not quickly make his appearance, Julia dreamt of being a career girl suffi-ciently successful to make it unnecessary for her mother to go on working. Julia hated to see her having to kneel down, her mouth full of pins, in front of a client, adjusting a pleat or a hem.

Pressed against each other, because the tables were small and the place crowded, they ordered two cups of coffee. Edith found herself looking at her young companion with an affection that seemed quite new to her. The disenchanted, cold, lucid cynic she thought she had become, was being irresistibly drawn towards what was fresh, honest, even naïve, in this pure young girl. It was as if she would have liked to be born again in the state of innocence that Julia represented. This was curious of course, because Edith had only known the girl three days, but the more she looked at her the more she was convinced that in Julia she was seeing what she herself had been only a relatively short time ago, before what took place after the wedding changed her.

'Only three days,' Edith said to herself. 'I have known her only three days and already I am terrified that we shall be parted, that she will be moved to a different department.'

Meanwhile Julia, unaware of what was taking place in her friend's mind, was smiling at a girl of her own age who had asked her to pass the sugar bowl. The café was hazy with a damp warmth that misted the curtained windows. It appeared to be the rendezvous of young typists and shop-girls who, unable to afford a real lunch, or even the semblance of one, made do with coffee and perhaps a roll. A girl absorbed in a library book, whose pages she feverishly turned with one hand while she nibbled a sandwich held in the other, wore spectacles with the thick lenses of the short-sighted. Into what world of romance had she flown, wondered Julia, who had immense pity for those who, like herself, saw almost everything and everybody through a veil of imagination, no lines ever being hard or clear. Edith, for whom action provided the stimuli of life, had no interest in books of any kind. She looked round the café, became bored, lit a cigarette and offered one to her friend. Julia refused, saying that neither she nor her mother smoked habitually—perhaps one cigarette on special occasions after a meal but probably not twice in three months. Edith smoked nervously, not really enjoying it herself, knocking imaginary ash off too quickly before it had time to form, called for the bill and insisted on paying for both coffees herself.

'Next time,' she said. 'Perhaps! We shall see. Today you are my guest.'

When Julia arrived in her department, Betty told her that Mrs Davies wished to see her. Julia was to go to her office as soon as Betty returned from lunch.

'Oh!' cried Julia, blushing with sudden fear and emotion. 'Have you any idea why?'

'None,' said Betty. 'But don't panic. I am sure it's for nothing serious.'

A box of new sprays and headpieces had arrived from Paris that day. Betty had spent the morning cataloguing and pricing them, and as soon as she had gone Julia set about arranging them. This work pleased her so much that, in spite of being constantly interrupted by customers, she quite changed the look of the department, giving it a brightness it had not enjoyed before. Even Betty was agreeably surprised when she came back.

'You have been busy!' she exclaimed good humouredly. 'I suppose you have not had a single customer!'

'On the contrary,' said Julia, laughing. 'I was even obliged to start a new order book. I have not forgotten what you told me—that the cash one takes is the only criterion of a good salesgirl!'

'Well, off you go,' said Betty. 'Take the lift behind the glove department. Mrs Davies and the dress buyer have adjoining offices on the restaurant floor. Good luck to you!'

Julia's heart was beating fast as she introduced herself to a secretary in an outer office.

'Go straight in,' said the secretary. 'Mrs Davies is alone.'

She found this elegant person seated on a high-backed chair behind a desk covered with samples of flowers and feathers sent by manufacturers from all over Europe, from Austria, from Italy, from France as well as from the English Midlands. She sat very erect, fingering her pearl necklace as she scrutinized Julia with a smile. Her hair was once again beautifully styled, and the electric lamp with its rose-covered shade standing on her desk made her rings sparkle. Julia became increasingly selfconscious under this examination and, in order not to blush and lose her poise, she centred her attention on a box of foreign-looking chocolates that lay in front of her.

'Take one,' said Mrs Davies. 'They come from Sacher in Vienna, a present from an Austrian manufacturer. Take one for Betty too.'

Julia would have preferred to refuse. She was not sure what to do with the two chocolates she had been invited to choose from the expensive box. She picked the two smallest and placed them delicately on the edge of Mrs Davies's desk.

'I asked you to come up,' said Mrs Davies, 'so that we should get to know each other better. I try to make the girls in my department understand that really and truly I am here to be disturbed at any time, not only if they have a problem connected with the store but one with themselves, their personal out-of-store-hour lives. Youth is such a difficult

67

time for a girl. It's lovely, of course, perhaps the most lovely time, but when I was your age I remember all too vividly how every tiny thing assumed enormous proportions. That was both the danger and the fun of it. First impressions are never again recaptured. Still, only those of us who have experienced it know how many things stand in the way of a girl's search for happiness.' She smiled. 'So you see that it is not only as a representative of the store that I am talking to you, but as myself, a slightly older, more experienced woman.' She paused. 'Do you still like the work? Do you think you will get on with Betty?'

'I like the work,' said Julia in a firm voice, 'and I think I shall get on well with Betty.'

'I am glad. I was very sorry to lose Janet, who was an excellent salesgirl and had initiative, which Betty, with all her qualities, occasionally lacks. Perhaps I should explain to you exactly what I mean by initiative. Initiative is to say frankly what strikes you about the merchandise and in what way customers react to it. When you have difficulty in selling something, when you are obliged to use a great deal of persuasion, that is the moment to come up and tell me. The smallest piece of information can be as vital to a store buyer as news of troop movements to a general in the field. If you wish to become a good salesgirl always imagine that you are not an employee but that you own the store.'

Julia was not quite sure what to say. She recalled Edith's burning desire to own a store of the same kind, but Julia was too modest to believe in miracles for herself. However, she felt certain that she had a gift for persuasion, especially when it came to selling goods to other girls.

'That is all I have to say,' said Mrs Davies. 'I am sorry to hear that Despatch will need you for a few more mornings, and I only hope that you will not be too disturbed by this division of labour. You must think of it as widening your knowledge of the store as a whole. Goodbye, Julia dear. Take your chocolates and give my love to Betty.'

'Thank you, Madam,' said Julia, rising to go.

Disdaining the lift, she ran down the stairs and met Francis for the second time that day.

'Again!' he cried joyously. 'Don't you ever do any work in this store?'

Sure of herself now, buoyed up by her interview with Mrs Davies, she said, shaking her golden hair:

'What goes for me goes for you!'

He looked back at her with surprise and admiration.

'What happened?' asked Betty as soon as she was back in the department.

'Nothing much,' answered Julia prudently. 'Mrs Davies merely asked if I liked being here. She gave me two chocolates that come from some famous Viennese confectioner called Sacher. Which will you have? I shall save the other for Mother.'

'She took a long time just asking you if you liked being here,' said Betty with the merest touch of resentment. 'She does have a tendency of course to butter up new girls. She was the same with Janet. I hate favouritism.'

'You are on the wrong track altogether,' said Julia, wrapping her chocolate in a small piece of tissue paper and slipping it into her handbag. 'The other question Mrs Davies asked me was whether we got on well together.'

'What did you tell her?'

'I said we got on fine up till now,' said Julia, going off to serve a customer.

She was late leaving the store and, as there was no sign of Edith under the fine rain that had not stopped all day, Julia put up her small red umbrella and hurried home alone. In Old Compton Street, by the foreign newspaper shop, she saw Iris, Daisy's young sister, some twenty yards ahead of her. She started to run, splashing mud on her stockings, and called out 'Iris! Iris!'

Iris stopped, recognized Julia, made a friendly sign to the effect that she could not wait, and disappeared in the direction of the Palace Theatre. What Julia had wanted to ask was whether she would be going, as she usually did, to the small dance club off the Tottenham Court Road where the three girls, Julia, Daisy and Iris, liked to meet while their mothers did the weekend shopping in Berwick Market.

That evening after a meal that Julia's mother had lovingly prepared, mother and daughter went to an American film they were anxious to see. Julia's mother knew all the Hollywood stars and avidly followed their pictures as well as news of their matrimonial affairs. Several times Julia was on the point of telling her mother about the all-important interview with Mrs Davies, but she checked herself because she did not want to hurt her mother's deep love for her by a too enthusiastic tribute to her buyer's cleverness and elegance. 'I will tell her in the morning,' she said to herself, but in the morning there was so little time and once again she was put off by her mother's pallid face and overtired expression. She was obviously working too hard.

Giving her mother the chocolate without revealing its history, she hurried to work. Edith arrived late in the basement, explaining that she had been sent by the head of her department to the stock room to fetch a number of dresses ordered by mail. 'I half expected to be kept up there all the morning,' she said. 'One of the girls in the department is ill. Personally I am delighted. This afternoon I shall have her customers as well as my own, so that for at least one day I should make double commission.'

'The poor thing,' said Julia, feeling the sick girl would need the money more than ever.

'She's a bitch!' said Edith. 'And who knows if she really is ill. As it's nearly the end of the week, more likely than not she has gone off to the country with a boy-friend.'

'Why are you so aggressive about the girls in your department?' asked Julia. 'What have they done to you?'

'Nothing individually,' said Edith. 'I am in the dress department because I asked to be transferred to it as it's the toughest department in the whole store. To get to the top in the dress department, especially in an expensive store like this one, is to get to the most worthwhile top the hardest

70

way. Another reason why I chose to work here is because, though women aren't always easy to get along with, I definitely don't want to work with men. If I had my choice I would have nothing more to do with them.'

'Oh?' exclaimed Julia, suddenly intrigued.

Edith stopped talking a moment, looked hard at Julia and went on:

'That wedding I told you about—the one at which I was so deliriously happy because I was one of the bridesmaids and all the world was new for me—it marked the beginning of what was to prove, at least temporarily, a wrecked life. Whether it will be like that for always, I cannot tell. Can one, after so great a tragedy, be re-born?

'I wanted to be the prettiest, the most looked-at, the most exotic girl there, with my dark eyes and long, black hair. Yes, believe it or not, I was radiant that day and my escort was none other than the bride's brother. He had just come back from what amounted to a world tour of spinning mills. His parents, their parents, I should say, owned a mill. He knew more than I would ever know. He was popular with men, he was a charmer with women, and he arrived at the ball, my first ball, smiling, handsome, sun-tanned and covered in all the glory of having just arrived from Japan. When he complimented me on my ball dress, there was magic in his words. His compliments, the music and the flowers, all went to my head and we danced together nearly the whole night through. People looked at us, saying "What a handsome couple!" My mother gazed at me with surprise. I think that secretly she was afraid of the happiness she read in her daughter's eyes. She had never really seen me until then—even less had my father seen me. Until then I had been merely a child to both of them.

'We had been invited to the wedding, as I told you before, because my mother had been to school with the bride's mother. But while the bride's parents owned a mill my father worked as an employee in a wholesale house, so that by provincial standards the social difference produced a slight embarrassment between us. Naturally, my parents

71

were proud that their daughter had been the subject of polite admiration at the ball, but their ambitions stopped there. They knew their places, as the old-fashioned saying went in that part of the world. As for me, I had no choice but to accept with a wry smile a few pointed remarks on the way home, and then the deadly monotony of the weeks that followed. I hung my beautiful ball dress in my wardrobe, and every time I looked at it I burst into tears. My father, who was not by nature ambitious, kept on telling me that we must all economize now to make up for the money my mother and I had spent as a result of my being a bridesmaid.

'Then one evening as I was walking along the quiet street where we lived a sports car drew up beside me and my beau of the ball called out: "Hello, Edith!"

'"Edward!"

'It was in my sudden joy that I called him Edward, though he had begged me to do so on that unforgettable night.

'"Jump in!" he said.

'Trying to curb my eagerness, I said:

'"What's the hurry after all these weeks? What made you suddenly remember me?"

'But after a little persuasion I jumped in and we drove out to some woods on the outskirts of the town. Though my conscience was not quite at ease at first, any feeling of guilt was soon submerged by the purr of the engine and the immense happiness of rediscovered love. Should I have allowed myself to be so easily won over? I was neither a prude nor amoral. I was just a girl tolerably well aware of the calculated risks that a girl without a fortune must take with the son of a wealthy family.

'After all, my mother had been at school with his mother. And does anything good ever happen to girls who stay at home every evening?

'We talked about the most innocent things. He told me he was bored living in the provinces, and he thought London the most exciting city in the world. He stopped the car in a deserted part of the road, and we walked hand in hand through the woods. I made a cowslip ball. His blue eyes were still full of the oceans he had crossed, and I thought him even more wonderful in the silence of the woods than in the glamour of the ballroom.

'After a while he looked at his wristwatch and said:

'"Forgive me, Edith. We must go back. I have an appointment in town. My father will be furious if I don't turn up."

'So we went back to the car and he drove me home in time for me to join my family at supper.

'After this, on spring evenings he often called for me and took me out in the car. If he claimed to have other appointments, or if I saw him with friends, I became appallingly jealous. He was the first man to kiss me. What we both felt during these long, delicate embraces, stolen in the depths of the country where lilac perfumed the air and the orchards were full of cherry blossom, was so utterly wonderful that though he never asked me officially to marry him, we both began to act as if we were engaged. Perhaps I should have been more insistent on this point, but a girl hesitates to risk hurting the man she loves and, strange as it may seem, I never came upon any reticence on his part. I had no reason to suppose that he wanted less than what we both so obviously took for granted. As spring turned to summer, as the cherries ripened and the first roses came out in the gardens, and strawberries appeared on their beds of straw, we went farther afield. We discovered new walks and inns where we could dine. In a village near Hereford, after we'd visited the cathedral, Edward ordered champagne for supper, and we spent the night as husband and wife in a picturesque half-timbered room. After this I loved him even more passionately, for he was teaching me, in addition to everything else, the joys of perfect companionship.

'Strangers began to talk to my parents about us. And then one morning, almost as soon as I had jumped out of bed, I began to feel sick and a cold sweat enveloped me as if in a vice. These symptoms, which I don't need to enlarge on, were repeated during the following days.

73

'Edward had gone to London, and life at home had become intolerable because of the silent enmity of my parents. On his return we met as usual. It was then that Edward told me that while in London he had been obliged to consult a specialist. He was affectionate and almost gay, but he drove me home much earlier than I thought necessary. My mother was making something in the kitchen, and she began to ask me questions that I didn't feel inclined to answer for the moment.

'I had just celebrated my eighteenth birthday. In spite of these vague fears that I might have been imprudently caught, I consoled myself by reflecting that I was in love, that as far as I could judge my love was reciprocated and that life, at least in its long-term prospects, was wonderful. All the same, the time had come when Edward must be made seriously to talk about marriage. That same evening on our way back from a road-house I told him that we ought to do something about it. The very word marriage that sounded so natural on my lips, so constantly and lovingly had I thought about it, produced a violent reaction. Was I so naïve as to think that our liaison had been anything more than a pleasant interlude for both of us? Modern girls no longer tried to trap men into marriage. They were too knowledgeable, too wide-awake, too well served by the pharmaceutical profession. At the university, and at almost every stage of his trip round the world, pretty girls had more or less thrown themselves at his head. They were too fun-loving and too sophisticated to deny themselves equal freedom with men. Quite apart from this he was practically engaged. Mills were amalgamating, smaller ones were being merged into larger ones, and there was this girl whom his parents wanted him to marry because it would make the financial situation so much easier. It was not that he was particularly in love with her at the moment, but he had been brought up to the idea that he would have to shoulder his responsibilities.

'His responsibilities! Just imagine! I had never seen this side of him, so cold, so cynical, so hard. He said: "Why didn't you take precautions? Other girls do." And then he stopped the car, took out a notebook and wrote down the name and address of an abortionist, as calmly as if he had been a doctor writing out a prescription. And while I sat beside him, the whole of my world falling in pieces around me, he tore off the page and handed it to me saying: "I'll bring you the money you will need tomorrow. Don't be a goose, Edith. It happens to millions of girls. You don't need to spoil everything." Then quite gaily he said: "Everything is made so easy these days!"

'When he dropped me at home I just couldn't believe that I would find the house and everything as I had left it. I expected the house, the people in it and the furniture to have suffered the same sort of change that had taken place in my heart. If my heart were shattered, then all the rest of the world must be shattered too. I was surely not strong enough to bear this thing alone.

'I thought about suicide. At college I had been amazed how often girls younger than myself talked quite seriously about ending their lives, even because of a failed examination. As Edward had said about abortions, everything was made so easy. What could be easier than too many aspirins, especially if taken with a lot of alcohol? But I was religious and I wanted to live. I found it hard to convince myself that I had done anything wrong. Had it been a crime to put my trust in a young man whose mother had been at school with my mother, at whose sister's wedding I had acted as bridesmaid, a young man I loved in the purest way, whom I admired and thought the world of?

'What increased my misery was that my mother obviously knew but was never brave enough to tell me so. I told myself that if my father were to hit upon the truth he might easily throw me out of the house. Such things did still happen. Indeed they were quite common in our part of the town in this enlightened age.

'A few days later Edward asked me to meet him at the bottom of our street. He handed me a tight roll of bank-notes and then gave me to understand that everything was over between us. During the rest of the evening at home I kept glancing at my mother and tried to read what was taking place in her mind. My young sister had gone to the pictures with a boy-friend. I would have liked to warn her, but what could I have said? When I saw other girls of my age in the street, in shops, at the office, I told myself how fortunate they were not to have this load weighing them down. I would gladly have changed places with any one of them. I began thinking of myself as different, like a girl on bail for a crime, and I found it more and more difficult to sleep at night. I hid the money Edward gave me, along with the sheet of paper, at the back of the drawer where I kept underclothes—though I could never be sure that my mother or my sister would not start rifling through my things as soon as my back was turned. In spite of his cynicism Edward was probably terrified of what I might say or do, for I was under age and it was in my power to ruin his future as he had ruined mine.

'I wondered if it would be possible for me to keep my child. And as this thought passed through my mind, I asked myself if Edward's sister was in the same condition as I was, and what she had done to deserve so much happiness while I was struck down, defeated. Was she kinder, more charitable? Was God rewarding her for acts of righteousness on the part of forebears three or four generations back? My forebears, for all I knew, might have lived the sort of lives for which retribution on the children and grandchildren could be exacted.

'For I was always coming back to the argument that though I might not be much better than other girls I could not be so very much worse, unless it was that I had loved too well. If that was a fault, then where was justice?

'My mother continued to look at me with curiosity and when, in the morning or at night, I kissed her, I occasionally had the impression that she tried to bury my face in the softness of her hair. I felt this so strongly and I was so much in need of compassion that if she had only opened her arms and pressed me to her I would certainly have been only too glad to tell her everything.

'A week later, on a Saturday, I put the wad of banknotes in my purse and took the 9.30 express to the city, fifty miles away, that was mentioned on the slip of paper Edward had given me. I chose an empty compartment and settled down in a corner seat and started to read a novel I had snatched up before leaving home. Of course I was much too on edge to concentrate, and I was almost relieved when two girls broke into my solitude at the only stop on the journey and noisily installed themselves opposite me. I still recall how they looked me up and down and then started laughing and chattering. They were on their way to attend a county dance and the elder girl kept admiring, and asking her friend to admire, the ring her fiancé had given her. He was a subaltern in a county regiment. She would be spending the night with his parents while her friend was going to stay with a married sister who appeared to have two small children. Her married sister, said the girl, was urging her husband to ask for a rise because she found it difficult to make ends meet because of the children. She no longer went to the hairdresser, she dressed shabbily and she was letting herself go. "She depresses me," said the girl.

'Their eager conversation helped me to forget my own troubles.

'As soon as the express ran into the noisy glass-domed terminus, the two girls opened the carriage door and ran joyously down the platform and I lost them in the crowd. I was one of the last to pass the barrier. My legs felt heavy and fear clutched at my throat. In the station yard a newspaper seller was calling out the midday edition of a London evening paper. "All the runners and prices!" he called. "Evening paper!" Timidly I showed him the address I had and asked if he could tell me the best way to get there. Half a dozen chocolate-coloured provincial buses were drawn up in the forecourt of the station. The man interrupted his monotonous yelling and told me to take the one with the letter A in front. "Ask the conductor," he said, "and don't let him forget to put you off because the stop nearest the street you want is not a scheduled stop but a request." I thanked him, and he said: "That's all right, Miss. Good luck!"

'At these words my heart melted. Why had he wished me good luck? What had made him guess that I needed a word of kindness? He was soon calling out his runners and prices again, whipping out a paper from under his arm every time a customer came along, throwing the coppers into a tin box at his feet.

'When I had seated myself in the bus and the driver had switched on the engine ready to move off, the newspaper seller looked up at me and smiled. Though there was too much noise to distinguish what he said I was pretty certain from the movement of his lips, that he was repeating the three words: "Good luck, Miss!" This might, of course, have been any cheerful newspaper seller's reaction to the worried look of a young girl appealing to him for help. My jet black hair and large eyes had accustomed me to the gay good mornings and occasional wolf whistles that any reasonably pretty girl is bound to receive. But this man's "Good luck, Miss!" were the first words of friendly encouragement that I had received from any human being since Edward had left me. What saddened me was the thought that this kindness had to come from a complete stranger.

'When I asked the conductor to put me off at the road mentioned on the paper, a young man facing me said: "I will show you, Miss. I am getting off there myself." This new piece of friendliness helped to steady me. My destiny that seemed to have been drifting for the last few weeks was now taking me nearer its completion with every throb of the bus's noisy engine. What had to be done was on the point of being accomplished.

'We left the centre of the city far behind, and for a time we went past small, respectable houses where the owners were mowing the lawn, or tending a rose bush in the small front gardens. Since it was Saturday my father would

78

probably be doing much the same thing, and I rejoiced at the thought that in a matter of hours, if all went well, I might be back home, delivered of my terrible secret, walking with my head held high, like a prisoner acquitted of a crime that might well have sent her to jail for a year, ten years, a lifetime.

'The young man in front of me rose, rang the bell and invited me to follow him. At the corner of a tree-lined suburban road, he left me, hurrying off in a different direction. The clinic was at the bottom of an unkempt garden, an ugly red brick house half hidden as I walked down the gravel path by the trunk of an elm. I pushed open the door that led into the hall and I was met by a nurse in white cap and apron. She asked me in such a rude tone what I wanted that I quite lost my self control and could only whisper the name written on the paper. "Oh!' she said. "This way, please."

'She left me alone for a moment. I was then put in a new panic by the sound of a baby crying in some distant room. Nothing could have been more unexpected or more harrowing in the circumstances. "I have come to the wrong place!" I thought. "What on earth shall I say to him?" However, within minutes, the nurse returned with the doctor mentioned on the paper, an elderly man, completely bald, who led me along a corridor into his office. He sat behind an untidy desk, and I sat erect, nervously clutching my handbag on my lap in front of him. "Who sent you to me?" he asked.

'I showed him the page from Edward's pocket diary. I had slipped it for safety inside my right glove so that the paper nestled against my palm. I had studied it so often that the edges were frayed. He looked at it carefully, took up his cigarette lighter, put a flame to the incriminating document and watched it burn itself out into a charred coil. Then he said:

'"Will you allow me to look inside your handbag?"

'"Why?"

'"Most women have a diary or an address book."

79

'"I have a diary," I said, "but I never write secrets in it. However, you are welcome to look at it."

'I handed him the handbag and watched him flick through the diary, fumble amongst my personal belongings, lipstick, powder compact, keys, etc. "There!" he said, giving it back to me. "I'm sorry to have to do that."

'"The roll of notes is for you," I said. "I have not even counted it. I assume that the person who sent me to you was aware of the correct sum."

'I handed him the tight roll and, scarcely glancing at it, he opened the top drawer of his bureau and dropped it in. Then he locked the drawer and put the key in his pocket. "Excuse me a moment," he said, getting up. "I will be back right away." I heard him preparing something in an adjoining room, and on his return he handed me a tumbler. "Drink this," he said. "It will help you relax."

'He then left me alone a second time, and I began to feel overwhelmed with tiredness. The heat of the room, the smell of disinfectant, the noise of the baby crying, the drink the man had given me, the way my heart beat—all this sent me drifting into unconsciousness. I remembered the laughter of the two girls in the train, the one who was going to spend the night with her fiancé's parents, and the other who would be staying with her married sister. Was the baby crying I'd heard on entering the house one of the married sister's babies? Was I perhaps going to the county dance too? Would I be going with the two girls in the train? Edward was crossing the room to offer me a glass of champagne. He had an arm round my waist, and now we were dancing to the strains of that wonderful band. What bliss to dance with Edward! Edward kept on whispering in my ear that I was the prettiest girl in the room, that my dress was beautiful and that he wanted to marry me. Then we were in a garden full of roses, and now we were walking arm in arm across a green lawn in the shade of tall trees, elm and beech and oak. We had left his sports car in a nearby country lane. Birds sang in the boughs of the trees. My mother was in the kitchen ironing the sheets she had just taken down from the line, but I would have to iron the handkerchiefs. My hair fell in waves to my waist and I longed for the day when I was grown up and could have it arranged in the latest fashion. "My beautiful, beautiful daughter!" said my mother, kissing me on the forehead and taking me into this wonderful store where she was to buy me a bra and a girdle and a white silk slip so that I should have proof that at last I was grown up. Was there anything in the whole world more wonderful than to blossom out into a young woman!

'A shiver woke me. I lay under a heavy blanket and I could not remember what had happened or where I was. I tried to shout and, though I was not aware of it, some sound must have escaped my lips because I heard a voice quite near me, saying: "Awake? That's fine. You can get up and dress now. There is an express train from the Central Station in just under an hour. I have made you a cup of strong tea with three lumps of sugar."

'I got up. I dressed. I drank the tea. I did everything I was told to do like an automaton. My head felt too light for my body, and I wondered if it would suddenly float away.

'When I was ready the nurse in the white uniform took my arm and led me to the top of the drive, reminding me where exactly the bus would stop. She left me there alone, obviously unwilling to be seen in my company. She said: "Don't worry. Everything will be all right, but try to take it easy tomorrow. Lucky for you it's Sunday."

'She probably knew about the time of the buses because she had scarcely left me when one arrived. The conductor helped me up and I dozed all the way to the Central Station.

'There were twenty minutes before the train was due, and so I went to sit on a hard chair in the waiting-room. My legs ached and I turned and twisted trying to find a reasonably comfortable position. Soon the pain was intolerable and it seemed wiser to go in search of the Ladies, but as soon as I tried to get up the pain redoubled and I had to grip the door handle to save myself from falling. The room was turning

81

round. If only the train could come in quickly so that I could hurry into it and feel that at last I was safely on my way home! I closed my eyes so that I wouldn't see the room turning.

'I was in bed feeling wonderful, and my mother was holding my hand. But she wore her anxious expression and as I wanted to reassure her I called out softly: "Mother!" She did not appear to hear. I tried to concentrate on a lamp with a blue shade, but the shade dissolved and I saw that it was the globe itself that was blue. I was back on the lawn with those tall trees and Edward, who was walking beside me with an arm round my waist, bent over and kissed me on the top of my head. I heard him asking: "Shall we dance?"

'My mother really was sitting by my bed. I became increasingly aware of this, but her face was hard and grim, drawn not only by fatigue but by censure. A nurse, who wasn't at all like the one in the red brick house but younger, prettier and with a very gentle voice, bent over me and asked if I felt better. My face was covered with warm tears. I cried so much that soon my pillow was wet with tears, but I simply could not stop crying. My mother and the nurse were talking together in low voices, and at last I heard the nurse say: "You can leave her safely with us now. She is out of danger. We will keep in touch with you by telephone." "Yes," said my mother, rising. "I shall go home." She gave me a frigid kiss on my damp forehead and turned her back on me. "I feel as if I never want to see her again," she said as she left the room.

'I began to remember about Edward and my journey to the red brick house, and I even got as far as my wait with the nurse at the bus stop and the unbearable pains in the station waiting-room. If I had not been dreaming, if it really was my mother who had walked out of the room, then presumably she had felt unable to overcome the shame I had brought on the family. Once again I was intolerably alone. The nurse with the gentle voice brought me something to drink, saying: "It will help you to sleep!" As soon as I had swallowed it I dozed off into another long spell of oblivion, a night when my nostrils smelt of ether, when I heard myself moaning.

'I was nearly a fortnight in hospital. My mother never came back to see me, nor my father, nor my sister. I had no visitors and no letters. On the last day Sister took me to Matron's office. I was to be sent to a convalescent home so that I could remain for a while under supervision. In addition to what Matron called my appalling imprudence, I had contracted, she said, a contagious disease from which I would need to recover fully before contemplating marriage.

'At her words sudden shame flowed over me and I think that what I wanted most was to hide in a corner and die. Matron called me her poor child. I had been given a blood transfusion. I had been on the danger list. Perhaps I might gain some small comfort from the thought that if it had not been for the abortion that had brought me to the hospital in an ambulance that terrible other thing, which now filled me with unutterable shame, might not have been discovered in time. But now that it had been diagnosed early, I would recover. Time and patience would help me to forget. "My poor child," she repeated. "My poor child."

'About a month later, on the eve of being discharged from the convalescent home where I was extremely well treated, I was handed a letter from my mother. In this she made it clear that it would be better for everybody if I were not to return home. She sent me as much money as she could afford, adding that if I sent her my address as soon as I was settled in new surroundings she would do her best to give me some more.

'I never did,' said Edith. 'She has no idea where I am.'

3

THE next morning a radiant Edith, arriving in a whirl at Despatch, fell upon Julia and embraced her with exclamations of joy.

'I have wonderful, wonderful news to tell you!' she cried. 'Something remarkable, something tremendous happened in the dress department yesterday afternoon.'

Still under the influence of the tragic story her volatile friend had recounted less than twenty-four hours earlier, Julia could scarcely believe this sudden metamorphosis.

'I am not even sure how long I can stay down here,' Edith went on, putting down her handbag and drawing up a chair. 'I may not be able to lunch with you. Things are in such a state of uproar.' She laughed. 'A great wind of mystery and intrigue is sweeping through the whole department. You can almost hear it whistling behind the dress racks and the mirrors. Honestly, I can scarcely keep a straight face.'

'For heaven's sake,' said Julia.

'It happened in the peak hour when the store was crowded. Mabel, the girl directly my senior, was in one of the fitting-rooms with a customer. It appears that the woman had insisted on trying on a dress a size too small for her. Mabel says she could not get her out of it. The dress had stuck, you see, and Mabel in a panic rushed to look for her superior. By the time she found her, a crowd that had been excited by the woman's cries had pushed their way into the fitting-room, and there in the confusion the woman fainted—or at least pretended to faint. They sat her on a chair and slapped her face and brought her a glass of water. As soon as she came to she began shouting at the top of her voice that somebody had stolen her handbag which had been full of money!

'In due course the house detective arrived and we were all endlessly questioned. We were even marched off one by one and searched. I need hardly tell you that they found nothing. Either the woman's handbag was stolen by a customer who took advantage of the confusion in the fitting-room or else, which is much more likely, the woman never had a handbag, and the whole thing was a put-up job to make a claim on her insurance or to sue the store. Technically Mabel committed a major fault by leaving the customer alone in a fitting-room. The first thing that a new girl in our department is told is to keep a close watch on a customer's handbag during fittings.'

'What will happen to her?' asked Julia, already feeling sorry for the unknown Mabel.

'Her mother telephoned this morning to say she's had a breakdown. She will not come back to us. She is to be transferred, at her mother's request, to another department. That is the big news I wanted to tell you. I am to be promoted. Isn't that wonderful? I step into her shoes and a junior will be brought in to take my place.'

She paused for breath.

'So this is my last morning in Despatch. Never again shall I be obliged to spend hours taking the creases out of tissue paper or addressing catalogues to provincial customers. I aim to double my commission. You are glad for me, aren't you?'

'Yes,' conceded Julia, 'I suppose I am.'

'Advancement,' said Edith pontifically, 'is the only thing that makes a job like ours worth while. Not to advance is to stick in a rut. I could no longer live without a constant fight and a spot of intrigue. I am not like those girls who wait patiently at the end of every queue. I fight for a place on the bus when it rains. I squeeze through the closing train doors during the rush hour in the Underground. It is exhausting but it is life. It's what makes living in London so desperately exciting. My experience with Edward drained me of pity.'

85

'I don't quite believe you,' said Julia. 'Did you not go out of your way to be nice to me?'

'You are different,' said Edith. 'You are so innocent and naïve. I felt an urge to protect you.'

In their excitement the girls had raised their voices so that Christopher and Francis, kneeling behind the draped mannequins they were preparing for the next window display, became suddenly interested. This scene did not go unnoticed by the girl from the General Office as she arrived with the usual letters and files.

'What has come over you all?' she asked, depositing her burden on the girls' table. 'Has somebody been left a fortune?'

'Not quite but nearly,' said Edith. 'I am being promoted. I am to replace a senior girl in the dress department who had trouble yesterday with a customer who claims that her handbag was stolen.'

'So that's where it happened!' said the girl from the General Office. 'There is quite a to-do this morning in the legal department. That's the second spot of trouble this last week. Those things usually run in cycles.'

Enticed by the sound of scandal the two young men rose from their kneeling positions and came towards the girls. Edith, faced with this new audience, recounted in detail the story of the alleged theft. The young men were less interested in Edith's words than in the sudden animation of her voice and gestures that showed them, perhaps for the first time, that a girl they had both taken for granted was actually a rare beauty. Their admiration was so obvious that the girl from the General Office decided to break the spell by pointedly asking Christopher if he had enjoyed himself at Roehampton. Her own boy-friend had been given two stalls for the ballet at Covent Garden. Otherwise, instead of going to *Swan Lake*, they would have accompanied him and his girl-friend to Roehampton. Julia made her own interpretation of this side-talk. She was beginning to feel vaguely interested in both Francis and Christopher and she wondered how serious Christopher's affair was with the girl he had taken out the previous evening. These social activities, Roehampton in early summer and the ballet at Covent Garden, contrasted strangely with the miserable evening she had experienced at home with her mother. Edith's story had quite overwhelmed her, and Julia was the sort of girl who is so sensitive that she lives with frightening intensity through the experiences of other girls. Edith's tragedy, both moral and physical, had made Julia quite ill, and she had not dared tell her mother about it for fear she might be told that Edith was not a suitable friend for a young girl. This was Julia's first important secret from her mother. Did it foreshadow a gradual parting of the ways?

'My innocence,' thought Julia, 'is not without a tremendous curiosity. In fact I am all the more curious because I've seen so little until now. I am not blasée. I am full to bursting point of pent-up enthusiasm. I am like a film negative not yet exposed to the rich colouring of the world about me. But now that the shutter is about to open, I want to see everything. I want to experience everything.'

The two girls were over-excited. They did very little, and what they did do was continually interrupted. Soon after eleven Edith was sent for by the head of her department. 'There!' she cried. 'There! It has happened. They need me in the department!' When, after an hour, there was no sign of her returning to the basement, Julia decided to leave a few moments early and surprise her mother during the lunch hour.

She found her mother about to sit down to a cup of strong tea and a piece of burnt toast. This frugal meal was set out on a cleared corner of her work table, and it suddenly brought home to Julia the weariness of her mother's lonely days, and the inadequate nature of her nourishment. In full daylight, too, her mother's features appeared more than usually drawn.

'Mother, you're not ill, are you?' she enquired.

'No, dear,' answered her mother, 'merely tired, absurdly tired. I get up exhausted, and the slightest thing that goes wrong during the morning assumes tragic proportions. I have to watch myself not to become short-tempered during a fitting with a difficult client. Dr Beer says that most of his women patients feel as I do at a certain time of life. I'm afraid we must philosophically accept these small feminine disadvantages. Though we can't entirely forget them we can at least not allow them to govern our lives.'

She looked at her daughter and added:

'You are still very young, but being a girl brings its own problems. I spend hours worrying whether the man you fall in love with will be worthy of you. Marriage, as the saying goes, is a great lottery. But non-marriage is a tragedy.'

'Oh!' cried Julia, pouring herself a cup of horribly black tea. 'Don't worry about that, please. I would never dare especially since . . .'

'Since what?' asked her mother, looking up suspiciously.

'Since nothing. I can't help hearing what other girls talk about at the store.'

'Yes,' conceded her mother. 'I thought you would. Listening to what other girls say is a form of experience. But it does not prevent one from making the same mistakes. For instance, I ought to find some way of preventing you from making the mistakes I made. To know so much without passing on one's knowledge seems so selfish and so wrong. But how can one do it? Bringing up a daughter is a terrible responsibility.'

Julia looked anxious.

'I supposed you would have preferred a boy. Would you?'

'No!' said her mother. 'I might have been prouder of a son. One always is. Wait till you have a child. But I prefer a daughter. One can gossip with a girl, gossip delightfully about shared feelings, about feminine topics, whereas communication is limited between mother and son. There is admiration on one side and respect on the other. Yes, but that is all.'

'I must run!' said Julia, afraid of being late.

As she raced down the stairs and into the street she felt a new, a different love for her mother throbbing in her veins. This lunch-time visit had been worth while. It exonerated her to some extent for having at least temporarily transferred too much affection from her mother to the girls at the store, particularly to Edith whose experiences now occupied so much of her thought. However, though life, as her mother had pointed out, was undoubtedly full of pitfalls for a young girl it was tremendously exciting. Julia felt as if she could not have too much of it. As she hurried through the picturesque parts of Soho, she caught herself almost skipping with joy. It was magnificent to feel so supple, so youthful, so light on her toes. The streets were so gay with lunch-hour crowds, strawberries and cherries on the barrows, exclamations and jokes being bandied about, and girls of her own age laughing and joking as they hurried along arm in arm.

As soon as she had relieved Betty, who hurried off for her lunch, Julia had the satisfaction of bringing off half a dozen quite important sales. She really had succeeded in injecting some of her own enthusiasm into her customers. Looking round, she became aware of Mrs Davies on whose carefully painted lips she noted an amused smile. The buyer, taking advantage of the lull, made a sign for her to come over. She had a list of altered prices for certain types of merchandise.

'You will notice,' she said to Julia, 'that contrary to what you might expect, I have put up the prices of many of the sprays and ornaments that we've had difficulty in selling. When something essentially pretty is too cheap customers are apt to be suspicious of it. They think they may have been wrong to have been attracted by it. They question their own good taste. "I should not have fallen for something so cheap!" they will exclaim, putting it down. By slightly increasing the price we will show them how right they were to have thought it pretty. We will help to give them faith in their own judgment. I don't mean by this that everything in the department should have the price increased. On the contrary. In many cases a high price, even if the merchandise is worth it, deters a prospective customer. In these cases we

89

should try to narrow the profit in order to get the line moving. That is the essence of good saleswomanship.'

While Mrs Davies was going through the list with Julia, she said almost confidentially:

'I chose Betty's lunch hour so that I could go over the list with you. Betty has a great dislike of change. She is extremely conscientious and prides herself on knowing the price of every object by heart. I can see her point. It is delightful when a customer asks the price of something, to be able to answer right away without having to consult the price tab. You, I fancy, are more subtle. I would like to think that as you become more experienced I shall be able to come to you for advice.'

Julia blushed.

Was this, she wondered, the beginning of success?

Summer holidays were beginning.

Edith went to Ostend. On the Channel steamer going over she saw amongst the holiday makers sitting in deck chairs along the ship's rail her Aunt Margaret, her mother's sister. Aunt Margaret had made what was considered a good marriage, and as a girl Edith had been fascinated by the rings she wore, rings which at this moment were glittering in the hot sunshine reflected on the calm, blue sea. Trying to escape recognition, Edith prepared to squeeze past, her head turned the other way. But Aunt Margaret was too quick and called out her name so loudly that Edith was obliged to pretend to be affectionately surprised. This was the first time since she'd left home that she had found herself face to face with a member of her family. A sailor, seeing her standing beside her aunt, brought her a deck chair, and as soon as aunt and niece were settled side by side they began to exchange news with caution. Aunt Margaret told Edith that her father, so maligned for his lack of ambition, had died from cancer the previous winter, sadly and miserably in a local hospital. Edith found it hard to picture the break-up of a state of affairs she had always known, the peaceful monotony of a family of which she had come to think of herself as the sole transgressor, the one upon whom all the bad luck in the world had exclusively fallen. For these past years she had stored up hatred in her heart for them but now, deeply affected by the news of her father's death, she felt a streak of discomfort and guilt at not having been at her mother's side in her moment of need. Without giving the impression of being too interested, she adroitly questioned her aunt first about her young sister who, it appeared, was engaged to a boy of whom the aunt knew little, and second about her mother's financial position. This, said the aunt, had considerably worsened since the death of the breadwinner.

'Now, my dear,' said Aunt Margaret, 'what are *you* doing? I am pleasantly surprised to see what a beautiful young woman you have grown into and what excellent taste you have acquired in clothes. Your dress is very pretty.'

Pleased by the compliment and relieved that her aunt appeared totally to disregard the reason for her break with the family, Edith revealed that she was now in the dress department of one of London's most famous stores.

'Then I will come to see you during my next visit to Town!' exclaimed Aunt Margaret.

At these words Edith's latent resentment against all the members of her family suddenly flared up. If Aunt Margaret wanted to snoop or perhaps even to take advantage of her niece's position in order to try to get a discount on a new model dress, then she would soon discover her mistake. She should never have given the name of the store. She should never even have told her that she worked in London. How easily even she, experienced as she believed she had become, could fall into a trap.

Aunt Margaret, who was more worldly wise, changed the course of the conversation. She touched lightly on such topics as current events, on the weather, on the many holiday makers on the ship, on how fortunate they were to have such a calm sea. Edith, whose only desire was to gather the slightest particle of news about Edward, whom she continued both to love and to loathe, wondered how her aunt could be so secretive and so false as not even to make the slightest reference to the great upheaval that had shattered her happiness. At last, she said angrily:

'Stop talking about the weather and the little waves on the sea. Don't be such a prude, Aunt Margaret. Why do you try to gloss things over? When I was in hospital, later when I was in the convalescent home, did you ever write? Did you come to see me? You were ashamed of me, weren't you? I was tainted like those girls who lie and steal? What has happened to Edward?'

'Edward is married to a banker's daughter. His father was killed last month in a car crash and Edward is now head of the firm. I don't know whether he is happy or not. It would make no difference either way. Your mother often talks about you, though with a certain detachment that I deplore. I'm not sure whether she's ready yet to forget the past. But you, Edith, will get nowhere by storing up vengeance or bitterness in your heart.'

'I have made a new life for myself,' said Edith. 'I exchanged the town where I was born for London and that was no mean barter. London is every girl's dream. There I am judged not on my past but on my merits. Besides, I am no longer bitter, except with those who hurt me when I was down and needed help. The girl I like best at the store is as naïve and trusting as I was when I first met Edward.'

'London undoubtedly suits you,' said Aunt Margaret. 'You were very pretty on the day of the wedding. But London has turned you into something quite different—into a real beauty! You see that I repeat my little compliment. I admit that we all treated you very shabbily when, in your own words, you were down, but I think perhaps you should now be the better placed to reflect that the person who is down at the moment is not you but your mother. She is a widow. She is not well off, and she is about to lose through marriage—and unless I am mistaken, not a very good one—her younger daughter. In your trouble you had youth to help you; in hers she has the opposite. She was too true and too just. That was always her fault. Why are you going to Ostend?'

'To eat shrimps and Belgian buns, and to get sunburned on the sand.'

'Alone?'

'Yes, alone.'

'It sounds sad for a girl, for such a stunningly pretty girl,' said her aunt.

'What did you do for your holiday? Did you have a nice time, Julia?'

'I did nothing,' said Julia. 'Mother was too tired. We stayed at home.' She laughed selfconsciously. 'We wished we could have been with you at Ostend. They say the sands are wonderful.'

The two girls met now for coffee every morning in the small Italian café behind the store. The days of their apprenticeship in the basement were over. Backed by Mrs Davies, who was impressed by her integrity and her gift for saleswomanship, Julia was becoming more important. There was talk of bringing a third girl into the department where the turnover had more than doubled. Edith also continued her rapid ascent, earning enough now to buy sophisticated clothes. She looked like an elegant buyer in embryo!

'I have met a charming boy!' said Edith.

'Oh!' cried Julia, impressed.

This changed everything. This might be the beginning of excitement for both of them.

'Where did you meet him?'

'With one of the girls I share the flat with—the one who is in love with the Harley Street specialist.'

Edith hesitated.

'You remember me saying that I did not want to have anything more to do with men?'

'I remember, but then suddenly you fell in love with this one? Is that it?'

'Well, not quite, but I caught myself wanting him to notice me.'

93

'So it worked and he telephoned.'

'How did you guess?'

'I did not guess. I just hoped.'

'It worked but I remained on the defensive, I was prudent. I did not want to start a second love affair that would end like the first one. Edward never thought me socially or mentally good enough.'

'Edward was a rotter,' said Julia. 'He was just plain not good enough.'

'This one telephoned and we met a second time. Then, Julia, I did something terrible.'

'What?'

'I began to show off.'

'What did you tell him?'

'I gave myself the sophisticated airs of a career girl. I told him I was attending classes to learn German and French so that I could become a buyer for a big London store. We had no sooner parted than the thought that I had become a cheap liar made me feel miserable. With Edward I had never been a liar or a thief. I remained scrupulously honest throughout. Now I must be more honest than ever. There only remained for me one way out of this lie. Can you guess?'

'No.'

'You are slow, Julia darling. I entered my name right away for a foreign languages evening class. By this time I am in the thick of it. I'm learning German and French with young business executives. I've been thinking what fun it would be if you could join me.'

She broke out into gay, wicked laughter.

'But the boy? Would you seriously marry him?' asked Julia persistently.

'Because he phoned me after a party? No! No! He's still a total stranger. I merely said to you: "I have met a charming boy." What interested me were my reactions upon meeting a boy I could perhaps fall in love with. How I started to preen myself, and how I told him that stupid lie.'

'But you would marry the right boy? After all, the first

time we met, I remember you telling me about the young man who, in your imagination, would give you a store.'

'Now,' said Edith, 'I am merely working in a store and sharing a flat with two other girls. This is one phase of my life. Just as when I first arrived in London that was another, different phase. Imagine what a miserable figure I must have cut when, after my mother had told me not to return home, I walked out of the convalescent home with a borrowed suitcase. I travelled to London in a crowded train and eventually landed up in a girls' hostel off Soho Square. The hostel was kept by a Scotswoman. I lived in a cubicle partitioned off from other cubicles by walls that did not reach up to the ceiling. Most of the girls had, like myself, arrived from the provinces; but there were also some Greek girls, and a German girl. Though none of us had any money we were like children electrified by the excitement of discovering the joys of freedom and the anonymity and colour of a great, throbbing, modern city. We all shared this immediate love for London. For nearly a year I lived happily in my cubicle. I still have the worn camel-hair dressing gown that my mother brought me at the hospital and which is practically all I have to remind me of my girlhood at home.'

'There will be a next phase,' Julia insisted. 'A phase after the present one.'

'Yes, marriage perhaps, a husband who loves me, a house of my own with trees, a garden and the cool, green lawns that I dreamt about every time I lost consciousness. There is really no other happiness for a girl, is there?'

'I don't suppose so,' said Julia. 'Love and not to have to worry too much about money.'

Julia now helped Mrs Davies in her choice of novelties, especially tiny diadems and crowns of diamanté inspired by the kind that ballerinas wear on the stage, enveloping clouds of white tulle and beautiful headpieces of orange blossom for brides. Neither Betty nor Julia had ever dared to try on what was destined for a bride, for they believed, like most girls not yet brides themselves, that this would

95

bring them bad luck; just as one must not try another girl's engagement ring on one's own finger, however much one longed to do so in order to see for a few seconds what it would look like.

One afternoon Julia caught sight of her mother in the department. This was not the first time that she had come and Betty, therefore, knew her. Indeed they had become quite good friends. Very timidly, as was so much in character, Julia's mother stood a little way off, waiting without impatience for Julia to finish serving a customer. As soon as the sale had taken place, her mother came diffidently over, and after a few unimportant remarks, told her that she had learnt something quite extraordinary. 'Daisy's family,' she said, 'is to leave our street.' She'd heard from the milkman that something had happened to Daisy and that they were all moving to another part of London.

While speaking in a gentle whisper Julia's mother lightly fingered a floral headpiece that she obviously thought pretty, and Julia, looking at her with great tenderness, felt suddenly very proud. 'Don't come home too late tonight,' said her mother without raising her voice.

'I've asked my friend Edith to come back with me,' said Julia. 'You will not mind, will you? I'm so anxious for you both to meet.'

'I shall look forward to it,' said her mother. 'Now I'll hurry home and bake you both a cake.'

As soon as she had gone Betty, to whom Julia's mother had given her sweetest smile, exclaimed:

'How youthful your mother looks, Julia. She should get married again.'

'Certainly not!' said Julia. 'I would not like her to bring a strange man back to the house. It would be terrible. Just think! I would probably lose her.'

'When you marry, she will lose you!'

'That has nothing to do with it,' said Julia. 'Besides, I have not even a boy-friend yet.'

'Neither have I,' said Betty in a burst of bitterness. 'I

don't seem to interest men and yet, Julia, I'm quite pretty, aren't I? Do I lack charm?'

Betty was certainly pretty, even unusually so; but she was pretty in a serious way and Julia, though she might be wrong about this, could not imagine Betty allowing herself to be kissed by a man on a street corner, as Daisy had done.

For weeks Julia had been nervous in case her mother would not like the friend she was, at last, bringing home. Edith's affection, guiding her through the marvels of a new, exciting, outside world, had become as vital to her as her mother's, which she occasionally caught herself taking too much for granted. She was delighted to note that her mother had not only made the promised cake. The supper she had prepared was already laid out on the table. There were cold tongue and strawberries and cream.

Edith was at her best, breaking out immediately into stories of the delights and pitfalls of her daily struggles in the dress department. She described several French and American models that her buyer had introduced that same day. Some would sell, she said, some would not. She sketched their salient details on the back of an envelope and, carried away by her immense enthusiasm, exclaimed: 'If I had been in her place, I would . . .' Julia trembled at these words, afraid that her mother would find her friend bombastic; but before long Edith was admiring a dress that Julia's mother was in the process of finishing for a customer. She examined it with such care, exclaimed about it with such obvious knowledge that Julia's mother was charmed. The girl had judgment and rare good taste. She recognized at a glance every hem or seam that had been hand stitched. The button-holing delighted her.

Over coffee it was the turn of Julia's mother to show a desire to impress. She was not only a splendid sempstress but a born story teller. She belonged to the generation who could look back on the days when young apprentices sang or told one another all the latest gossip in vivid language. This business of Daisy and Daisy's family intrigued Julia's mother to the utmost degree. After leaving her daughter at the store that afternoon she had stopped to listen to what the neighbours were saying at the top of the street. She was overcome by what she had gathered and, knowing that Edith would be as concerned as Julia, both girls working in the store from which Daisy had so mysteriously disappeared, she said:

'She was too elegant. Did her departure excite any interest?'

'Not much,' said Edith. 'The girl we rather like, the one with whom Daisy worked in the General Office, merely told us one morning that she had left. What was she supposed to have done?'

'The silliest thing,' said Julia's mother. 'While she was opening the firm's mail, which apparently she did every morning, she stole an uncrossed postal order and thought she would be able to cash it at Leicester Square post office on her way home. She did not even need the money. With her fast shorthand and faultless typing she could get any job she wanted.'

'Did they prosecute?' asked Edith, who had seen enough in the store to know what anguish that can mean to a girl.

'The case came up one month before her eighteenth birthday,' said Julia's mother. 'She was saved the disgrace of being sent to jail, but it led to a punishment just as great. The boy who was about to marry her was forbidden by his parents to do so.'

'Did she love him?'

'I think so. He was a nice boy from an excellent family. This was the one thing that parents who have high principles could not close their eyes to.'

'Why do you say the one thing? Was there another?'

'Yes,' said Julia's mother. 'Everybody in the street had been commenting on the fact that Daisy continued to go to work in that red coat of hers—even in June when the heat was stifling, and after all the other girls in the neighbourhood, you Julia included, wore cotton dresses.'

'I was envious of that red coat of hers,' said Julia. 'It was beautifully cut.'

98

'Gossip flies along a street,' said her mother. 'It appears that everybody knew about it except Daisy's own mother, and maybe you two girls.'

'My goodness!' exclaimed Edith with feeling. 'How awful for her!'

'Not necessarily,' said Julia's mother. 'She gave no sign of not wanting a child. She may have thought, at least before the court case, that her condition might even hasten her fiancé in leading her to the altar. People say that he really was on the point of doing so. After all, it would not be the first time that a girl has hastened her marriage by being pregnant, and often such marriages prove in the long run to be very happy ones. Men are slothful by nature. They need to be spurred on. At all events when that silly business at the store broke out there were violent quarrels in the family.

'It is said that Daisy chose as her confidante an incredible character known in the street as "Old Madam", who lodges on an upper storey of the house occupied by Daisy and her family. Daisy's mother was always inviting her down, partly out of pity and partly to listen to the old thing recounting her latest extravagance.

'She was usually to be found with the family in their basement after lunch on Sundays. I do not need to describe to you, Julia, what a strange and picturesque ritual this Sunday lunch in Daisy's family has always been. The whole family gathers round the table. At the head sits Daisy's father wearing a white shirt, with the sleeves rolled up, and linen trousers that have been washed so regularly for so many years by his wife that they have become soft and as comfortable as silk.

'He sits on no ordinary chair but on an old brown leather armchair whose springs collapsed long ago under his weight. He sits there like Henry the Eighth scowling at his women assembled round the table.'

Edith listened with genuine pleasure to what Julia's mother was saying. Julia noticed with pride that her mother, carried away by her tale, had become prettier and much more youthful and gayer than she had appeared for a long time past. Clearly she was putting herself out to captivate Edith, and Edith was responding. Julia caught herself feeling almost jealous that her mother should be shining like this not to impress her but her friend. This was not quite what she had expected. Julia's mother continued:

'Into this family circle this extraordinary character called Old Madam had insinuated herself. She is a woman of many occupations and deep secrets, but part of her legend is based on the fact that every Saturday morning she goes to that hat shop opposite the Jewish bakers in Berwick Street to buy a new hat. She is never seen without this hat until she has chosen its successor the following Saturday.'

'But what does she do with the old ones?' asked Edith, laughing.

'That is precisely where her craftiness comes in,' said Julia's mother. 'After she has made her choice she can be seen coming out of the shop and turning into Brewer Street, between the barrows laden with fruit and vegetables, with the new hat on her head and the old one in a paper bag. Any other woman would continue to wear her old hat till she got home and carry the new one. But not Old Madam. At exactly half past one she can be seen making her way down Windmill Street, past the matinée queues in Shaftesbury Avenue, to the theatre where she has been employed for years as head attendant in the ladies' cloak-room. Before the end of the evening performance she has practically always managed to sell the old hat at a small profit. The money she makes allows her to repeat the operation the following Saturday.'

'She is certainly astute,' said Edith. 'Did she boast of her success?'

'Daisy's sister Iris discovered her manœuvre,' said Julia's mother. 'The fate of the discarded hats had intrigued her for a long time. She had imagined that Old Madam kept them locked up in her room, ranged in some cupboard, like Bluebeard's wives. Nobody in all the years that the strange old woman had lived on the top floor had managed to get into her room, however. But Iris managed to steal the old woman's key one day and look in.

'The room was full of strange souvenirs, foreign playbills and various mementoes of some long-ago Paris exhibition, but there was not a hat in sight. The following Sunday after lunch Iris, who was only sixteen at the time, put the question boldly to their guest: "Please, Old Madam, tell us what you do with your discarded hats?" Her voice was clear and demanding, in spite of the fact that her father was at the head of the table as usual and that she was terrified of him.'

'What did the old woman say?' asked Edith.

'She told the story as I've told it to you. Everybody laughed. They admired the old thing for the way she had solved the problem of always having a new hat which never cost her a penny, and they decided that Iris had shown considerable strength of character in being the only person brave enough to put the question point blank. Afterwards Iris told her mother about peeping into the room and about the French playbills. All this gave the family the idea that Old Madam must have had strange adventures on the Continent. Perhaps there was something sinister attached to her nickname.'

Edith was making herself so very much at home in their small flat that Julia had the impression that perhaps something that Edith represented had hitherto been lacking. If her mother occasionally appeared drawn or tired it might well be that she needed some new stimulus in addition to that which her own daughter could give her. Not a new husband, Julia found herself quickly thinking, but merely a different pair of ears to listen to her stories, perhaps even to her fears and hopes—and her occasional bouts of despair.

Edith, for her part, was obviously not insensitive to this atmosphere of family life which a young girl living in a flat with other girls occasionally misses, however amusing and youthful that sort of life can be. The fact that Edith, as she sometimes boasted, had a past made her react understandingly to these small feminine nothings that assumed in most women's lives a frightening predominance. Even the newest, most liberal laws men made to simplify what was so unsimple left a thousand problems and permutations that complicated Julia's or Edith's world.

'Perhaps,' Julia's mother went on, 'Old Madam guessed that Iris had stolen her key. She showed no resentment. What she very quickly guessed when the first warm days of spring came along was that a pretty girl like Daisy, slim as an elf, with shapely legs and trim ankles, does not willingly wear a red woollen coat, especially if all the other girls in their gay cotton dresses look like flowers in a garden.

'It was vital to hide the truth from Daisy's father. The family call him the "monarch", and he is not at all the sort of man to listen sympathetically to female problems. When he is angry, he is quick to whip off his belt, the one, Julia, with the square buckle, and let fly at his wife and daughters. If people think men do not beat their wives any longer, they are wrong. When the poor woman who had been so slow to notice her daughter's condition became aware of it she kept on moaning: "Something must be done to prevent him from finding out!" She said to Old Madam: "He would go for us all! Every time he talks to a neighbour in the street I feel certain he will hear about it, and there is always the risk of him overhearing some allusion at the pub. It is always us women he goes for. Everything that happens is my fault or that of the girls."'

'Oh, I do pity Daisy,' said Edith. 'At the store I was prejudiced against the girls who work in the General Office, the typists and the secretaries. I thought them snobs. This changes my point of view.'

'Daisy and her sister do tend to be snobs when all goes well with them,' said Julia's mother. 'Daisy especially.'

'What do you suppose Old Madam feels about it?' asked Edith. 'What can she offer Daisy at this stage?'

'At this stage, sympathy,' said Julia's mother. 'She takes her to burn a candle at St Patrick's in Soho Square. There is nothing that anybody can say about that. The monarch himself was brought up by the Jesuits, and though he no longer goes to Mass he likes his wife and daughters to do so, as long as the Sunday lunch does not suffer! When they want a new dress, they tell him that it is to impress the neighbours in church.'

'Does he believe them?'

'Yes.'

Julia's mother said suddenly:

'Being a woman is terribly complicated. I keep awake at night thinking about Julia, worrying about the responsibility of having brought a girl into the world.'

Edith took a packet of cigarettes from her handbag, offered one to Julia's mother and soon they were both reflectively smoking. 'Really,' thought Julia, 'Mother is quite a different person this evening. She is trying to warn me about all sorts of problems while pretending not to.'

Getting up to examine again the dress that Edith had admired, Julia asked:

'Who is this dress for, Mother?'

'That very elegant woman from Maddox Street who comes to see you sometimes at the store. I made her a black velvet sheath last winter. Do you remember? She had ordered it to set off her beautiful blonde hair, though it does not satisfy her to be a natural blonde.'

'She must be very slim,' said Edith, allowing her eyes to rest greedily on the dress.

'She is,' said Julia's mother, 'but it so happened that today when she was trying it on, I felt obliged to point out that she had thickened somewhat in the waist. I did not want her to think that I was trying to skimp on the material. "I know," she answered very quietly. "I got caught. I'm two months gone." "Oh!" I exclaimed, taking my scissors to unpick. "I shall have to give you an inch or more." "No! No!" she said. "Do not alter a thing in this darling little dress. I positively adore it. As for the waist, the temporary thickening will have gone by next week. My doctor will take care of it. Meanwhile"—she gave me an odd little smile—"I am having what you might call a holiday. I do not need to take any precautions at all."'

'Most of us are not so sophisticated,' said Edith, with a touch of bitterness.

Julia much admired the slim blonde who, because of the friendly relations she entertained with her mother, quite often came to look up her daughter in Artificial Flowers. She liked her gentle voice, her understanding smile and the way she treated Julia with affectionate respect, as if she guessed that in a few years Julia might turn out just as successful and as well groomed and elegant as herself. Also, Julia had come to believe that every time her mother's client came to see her at the store she brought her good luck. This woman who was admired so much by men had an equal gift for making herself liked by her own sex.

'The client from Maddox Street,' Julia reflected, 'had probably learnt in a hard school to acquire this chic and to radiate this charm.' Nothing ever happened by accident. In order to earn enough money to bring up Julia her mother had done all this sewing, often to the detriment of her health; Edith had embarked on a new life by teaching herself to analyse the sales potential of a dress; Mrs Davies had equipped herself to become a career girl; and the woman from Maddox Street had this positive genius for exuding sex appeal. Nevertheless, the stories that Julia's mother had been recounting since supper were beginning to sap Julia's resistance and, as if one could suffer pain vicariously or by mere suggestion, she pressed her knees tightly together, wincing. These things which obviously could so easily happen to oneself were passionately interesting but they filled her with alarm. No wonder that women spent their lives discussing the various mutations of the same subject.

'My goodness!' exclaimed her mother, hearing the clock strike midnight. 'Edith will miss her last bus.'

'No bus takes me direct,' said Edith, laughing. 'Unless I hurry I shall miss not one but three separate buses!'

She got up, took her compact and lipstick out of her handbag and started to do what was necessary to her make-up. While painting the outline of her lips, she said: 'The girls in my flat will imagine that I have spent the evening riotously with a new boy-friend and yet, though we have done nothing but sit here and talk, I have seldom spent such a wonderful evening.'

Julia's mother exclaimed:

'Why don't we put you up for the night in Julia's room? Julia can sleep on the couch in my room as she often does.'

'Oh, let us do that!' said Julia. 'Tomorrow morning Edith and I can go to work together.'

Though Edith might not have admitted it, the return to her part of London alone at this time of the night was an ordeal she in no way looked forward to. She was afraid of dark streets. The idea of being pampered by Julia's mother delighted her.

She kicked off the high-heeled shoes she had just put on again, and watched Julia's mother pour the milk into a pan to make bed-time chocolate.

Some mornings feel empty and disappointing, even for a pretty girl in a crowded store where she is surrounded by desirable clothes and tempting accessories. Perhaps because of what she had listened to the previous evening, Julia was troubled by a vague unrest, as if something inside her was longing to break out from a world too exclusively filled with women.

The quick walk that morning through the streets of Soho with Edith on their way to work had not produced the expected magic. With Edith staying overnight, with Edith at breakfast, Julia felt that she had by now had more than enough of Edith. Edith's conversation, even her compliments, were getting on her overwrought nerves.

'You are fortunate,' Edith had said as they cut through Wardour Street, 'to have such a youthful mother to whom a girl could tell everything. It is really most unfair. What good will it ever do to you? Anybody can see that you are a born innocent. It is written in your face. Why could I not have had a mother like yours? We ought to be able to choose our parents, or maybe exchange them.'

'I am not a bit sure,' said Julia, trying to hide her ill

temper, 'that my mother would be particularly sympathetic if I was obliged to wear a winter coat in the middle of June to hide my condition. Last night she was trying to show off and, at the same time, to warn me about the perils that surround her daughter. As for your suggestion that anybody can see that I'm an innocent goose, thank you very much, but maybe you are wrong about that too.'

Between sales in her department that morning, Julia felt again the sting in Edith's remark about her being a born innocent. She flushed with anger. Edith was wrong. A girl could have, as Julia undoubtedly did have, an awareness gleaned not only from her mother's experience but from the conversation of her mother's clients, without her wishing to depart in any way from a certain puritanism that Edith had failed to detect in the often uncompromising character of Julia's mother.

What in fact had Edith meant? Was it really written all over her face that she was an innocent goose, and did this imply a lack of whatever was needed to attract a man? On the pretext that she wanted to wash her hands after dusting the back of a showcase, Julia ran down to her locker. 'I won't be long,' she said to Betty, and as earlier in the morning she had complained of feeling unwell and of the wave in her hair not remaining in place, Betty gave her an understanding nod.

Under the hard lighting Julia peered earnestly at her reflection in the mirror. Obviously this was not a good day. She looked terrible. Her sleep had been disturbed again by one of those recurring dreams about her mother dying. On every occasion Julia's unreasonableness caused this tragedy in her dream. She thought of herself as having become too demanding. She was usurping a place to which she had no right. On the grounds that by going out to work every day Julia had become the breadwinner, in spite of her mother's dressmaking, she took it for granted that on her return in the evening she would find supper all laid out and waiting for her. She had become lazy and untidy, leaving her clothes lying about her room, confident that as soon as her back was turned her mother would pick them up and put them lovingly away. Was this not asking too much of the woman she loved most in the world? How selfish Julia had become! Did her mother not do all the washing and ironing, all the housework?

The evening that Edith had spent with them had upset the calm uniformity of her home life. That pain she had experienced last night because of all those stories of abortion had not been entirely imagined, but the cause was not what she had thought. The discovery that she had her period explained it. In spite of the fact that she looked terrible, it struck her that Daisy would gladly change places with her at this moment.

Julia turned off one or two of the strong electric lights that flooded the mirrors and gave her that pallid appearance. Now she looked less frightening, but what she desperately needed was a cup of strong black coffee. Edith, who might have gone with her to the Italian café round the corner, was presumably busy in the dress department, putting new models on wax figures and arranging others in long cupboards. Edith, she decided, was showing signs of accumulating all the over-eagerness in business that she had condemned so violently until now in her superiors. She was turning into a department octopus, trying to run the entire floor. She spoke of making a triumphant return one day to her home town to surprise what remained of the family that had spurned her. The idea of this triumphal return amused Julia. The triumph of having become what? A girl employee in a gown shop? Compared with what had happened to Edward who, according to Edith, was now the owner of his father's mill and allied by marriage to a banking firm, how insignificant it sounded! How could people, even in this enlightened age, seriously talk of equality between the sexes?

'I will have to do without a cup of strong coffee,' thought Julia, reflecting on Mrs Davies's good fortune in having such a luxurious office, a table covered with flowers, boxes of chocolates and, in an adjoining office, a private secretary who would run and fetch her coffee and biscuits from the customers' restaurant on the same floor at a moment's notice.

Turning on her heels, Julia gave herself a final look in the full-length mirror against the far wall. She had well-shaped legs and slim ankles, the sort that only Anglo-Saxon and Nordic girls have. The black dress her mother had made her, with the pleated apron effect in front, was both slimming and becoming. The pleated apron, which was detachable, gave the dress an air of lightness. What would complete the general effect would be to borrow Mrs Davies's pearl necklace. She broke out into happy laughter.

Betty would be wondering what had happened to her. As soon as one left a department in which there was not a single customer, one could be sure that a moment later business would become brisk. She must hurry. At times Julia felt that her movements were slow, even lethargic, but there could follow swift acceleration. She could break from a trot into a gallop. Was this due to sudden impulse?

Impulse might be a good name for a new scent. It would be fun to be transferred to the perfumery department. She would marry a young man who created famous perfumes for the international market. Julia would design new forms of cut-glass bottles. Creation was the opposite to obedience. She would not have to take orders from anybody any longer.

She had forgotten all about Betty! Julia tore up the stairs, and arrived breathless in the department where, as she had feared, there was a crowd of customers. Betty shot her a furious look.

Julia set to work quickly and, while Betty was occupied with a provincial customer who was clearly in need of guidance, she was able to attend to a group of girls who had already chosen what they wanted, and were merely waiting for her to make out their bills. While doing this she became aware of a young man in a bowler hat and striped trousers who had collected several sprays at random and was holding them in one hand, while with the other he leaned on a tightly rolled umbrella that had his initials on a gold band on the handle. Julia could see that Betty had an eye on him, but she continued to be harassed by questions put to her by the provincial customer who broke into Betty's answers from time to time to explain which of her intended purchases were for herself and which were gifts for her friends. 'I only come up to London once or twice a year,' she said. 'Please put everything I buy into separate carrier bags with the name of the store outside so that I shan't fail to make an impression tonight when I step off the train.'

Normally, Betty rather liked this sort of customer, and she went out of her way to make herself pleasant. But this morning she continued, off and on, to eye the young man who obviously was something in the City. Perhaps a member of Lloyds or a stockbroker. Julia herself did not feel in any hurry, even now that she was free, to serve him. She thought that a man looked slightly ridiculous holding girls' frail headpieces and bridesmaids' posies, but, at the same time, he intimidated her just because he was a man. He was out of place, she decided, and gave her the same feeling of slight embarrassment as when she suddenly discovered that her slip showed under her dress or that a shoulder strap had snapped, endangering the poise of her bra.

'Do these sprays come from Paris?' the provincial customer was asking Betty. 'If you can assure me that they do . . .'

'I assure you,' said Betty.

Because Julia was unable to leave a customer unserved, she smilingly held out a hand for the headpieces and posies, and said:

'May I help you?'

'Yes,' said the young man cheerfully. 'I feel as if I were drowning. Why does a man appear so foolish in a place like this!'

He looked at her with amused curiosity:

'You are Julia, I presume?'

'How on earth. . . .?' she started.

'Tell me, Julia, did you have an amusing time last night?'

'Last night?'

Who was he? What was he driving at? How did he know her name? She had definitely never seen him before. She looked round quickly. The management was strict about private conversations between a salesgirl and a member of the opposite sex. It would never do for Mrs Davies to think she was breaking the rules. Julia did not want the elegant buyer to lose confidence in her. The store detectives might also be about. Julia was horribly embarrassed. All these considerations had no weight with the young City man who reiterated his question:

'Yes, last night.'

'I never went out last night,' Julia said in her most determined voice, as if this statement was sufficiently conclusive to put an end to the argument. 'I stayed at home with my mother and a girl-friend from the store. There now!' she said defiantly: 'Are you satisfied?'

'Yes,' he said, smiling. 'Quite satisfied.'

He took a visiting card from his wallet and handed it to her. 'Ah!' she thought. 'Now I shall know his name!' But it was not his name. It was the name of a woman with an address in Regent's Park. The young man said:

'Please have everything sent to the person at this address. In a box all done up nicely in tissue paper with a ribbon round it. It is for a young lady who is going to her first important party, a niece of mine. She is only ten but she knows exactly what she wants, and as her mother was too busy to choose them for her I offered to do so in her place. It was gallant of me, don't you think?'

'Very gallant,' said Julia, smiling.

'Take especial care of the small diadem of gardenias. She wants to look like a ballerina on the stage!'

He left her, and as soon as Betty was free she arrived avid for news.

'Who is he? What did he want?'

The two girls, as if searching for something, bent over the open drawer in which they kept their purses and various odds and ends. Their heads were close together. In this way they could exchange personal intelligence without appearing to gossip. 'He knew my name,' said Julia. 'He said: "Tell me, Julia, did you have an amusing time last night?" That was not natural, was it?'

'It's an old trick,' said Betty, not altogether sorry to deflate her companion. 'He must have heard me calling out to you when you came back from your locker. Some men are quick to make use of information they overhear. He probably likes blondes.'

'He didn't strike me as being the sort of man who would make a habit of doing that,' said Julia. 'Something amused him about me. He was keeping something back. Besides, you never did call out to me. You merely shot me a reproving look as if I had been away too long, which incidentally just isn't true. I hate feeling myself tricked or involved against my will in a mystery.'

'Oh! For heaven's sake,' exclaimed Betty, remembering how her former assistant had run away with a man right under her nose. 'Don't start getting romantic. One absurd young man with a bowler hat and a rolled-up umbrella doesn't make a summer.'

Waiting for Edith after work had become a ritual for Julia and the prospect bored her, but she was too young even to think about giving offence, so she would wait as usual in front of the store's first display window near the bus stop in Regent Street. Opening her handbag, she started searching diligently inside it for the aspirin she felt sure was there. The usual crowd of home-going employees and late shoppers surged round her. What she most wanted was an early night.

'There you are!' said Edith with the sharp edge of annoyance in her tone. 'Why must you keep your head down like that? I nearly missed you in the crowd. I am in a frantic hurry. Would you mind if, for once, I left you right here at the bus stop and jumped on the next No. 6?'

'Is something wrong?' asked Julia, vaguely sympathetic.

'This business of waiting for telephone calls makes me

ill,' said Edith, glad to talk about her worries. 'I rang the flat at lunch time. There was no answer. There never is a girl in the flat unless one of us happens to be ill, or out of a job or goes back to change. But he rang, I'm certain he rang. He may even have rung last night. I told Agnes if he rang to tell him that I had gone round to your place for supper. I never thought of it when I agreed to stay the night. I ought to have given Agnes a ring this morning from a call-box in Soho before she went to work. There's a No. 6! So long, Julia.'

'So long, Edith!'

'Well,' thought Julia as Edith forged her way through the queue and took the bus by assault, 'it looks to me as if we both wanted to give each other a miss tonight. I am tired of her stories and she is tired of mine.' Continuing to search along the bottom of her handbag she came upon the needed aspirin, swallowed it with a grimace and as much saliva as she could muster, and turning her back on Regent Street, began to walk through the narrow streets towards Soho.

When she came in sight of the tailor's shop owned by the parents of Daisy's boy-friend she saw his younger brother at the top of the ladder repainting the front. Above the door was written: 'Bishop and Sons—Ladies' tailors—Repairs —Remodelling.' 'Why couldn't Mother have a shop instead of having to receive her customers in a bedroom?' thought Julia. Could it be that even dressmaking was a man's business? Though in Paris a few women reigned supreme in a world of dressmaking, they were easily out-numbered by men. This, perhaps, had always been the case since the world of Worth. In every profession men were invariably found at the top. She felt angry and ashamed when people referred to her mother as a 'little home dress-maker'. In Julia's eyes her mother was something of an undiscovered genius. Her ideas merely needed to be brought to light, as a diamond was hewn out of rock.

'Nice to see you,' said young Bishop, descending from his ladder and offering her one finger of the hand that was not holding the paint pot. Julia said:

'Somebody told me you had gone abroad?'

'To Rome,' he answered. 'I served an apprenticeship with an Italian cutter in the Via Vittorio Véneto. Boy! Do those cutters know how to cut! I've come back bursting at the seams (forgive the pun) with European ideas!' This assertion did not particularly impress Julia, for whom tailoring was a male art quite distinct from sewing as her mother and her mother's friends understood it: embroidering, puckering, flouncing, inventing pretty turns or folds, and making do with the least possible material. Sewing for Julia was this delicate, feminine art. She even made her own lingerie. Tailors were elderly men who sat cross-legged in basements that could be seen through slanted plate glass windows as one walked along Savile Row and Cork Street, an underworld of flatirons, hats made from an old newspaper for bald heads and heavy bales of tweed and herringbone cheviots for City men.

Young Bishop said: 'Just now I am helping Father.'

'By painting the shop front?'

'Irony does not suit you, Julia. Father is a born cutter. I never realized just how good he was until I went to Rome, but he lacks the qualities of an innovator. That is where I must step in. I am going to show him how to adapt his experience to modern requirements. Soon I shall blot out the words Repairs—Remodelling and double our prices. We shall be leaders. I have my eye on an empty shop at the bottom of a new block going up near here. We shall have lots of light and a constant stream of potential customers. Father says that as I undoubtedly show signs of inheriting his qualities, he will show me how to add to them my own.'

Julia agreed that it sounded wonderful and that she was glad for him. All this was beyond her, however. There was something that she desperately wanted to know but dared not ask. For the sake of politeness she made a few tentative enquiries about the prettiness of Roman girls.

'As an Englishman,' said young Bishop, grinning broadly, 'I must admit that I was given one or two admiring glances, but all the same it was time I came home. I guess my parents were glad to have me back. I found them pretty upset about my brother's entanglement with Daisy.'

'Ah!' said Julia, having brought him round to the subject that had a really vital interest for her and for her mother. She waited. This was dangerous ground. She must assume an attitude of polite sympathy in the hope that he might enlarge on the involvement. She did not want him at this stage at any rate to treat her as being on the other side of the fence, on Daisy's side—though that, she reflected, would be what he would instinctively do, remembering that Daisy was her girl-friend and that girls usually stick together, as boys do when they are attacked. The brief silence between them may have imbued the younger Bishop with just those feelings of caution that Julia feared. He said: 'My brother Alan is not in this line of business. He takes after his mother.'

'Your mother,' corrected Julia.

'Yes, *our* mother,' said the young cutter. 'Mother was a teacher before she married Father. Tailoring was not her idea of maintaining a proper social status. Our trade is apt to be looked down on because of its connection with sweated labour and mid-European refugees. As it happens, I would say that my parents' marriage turned out a good deal better than most marriages. Mother and Father never cease saying that they are as much in love with each other today as when they were engaged thirty years ago. But my brother, ever since he was a kid, had a studious side. That is why we say that he takes after Mother. Without actually being ashamed of us he wanted to better himself. You might say that he is ambitious.'

'As a matter of fact,' said Julia, 'Daisy told me. She said that he was still young and unable as yet to earn his own keep but that he wanted to become something in the City. I forget what. I'm not even sure that she told me.'

'Well,' said the young tailor, 'she could scarcely expect her entanglement with him to work out in the circumstances, could she?'

'I have not seen her since,' said Julia, 'and I'm not sure

114

what you mean by the circumstances. I am just terribly sorry for her.'

The young tailor looked thoughtfully at his paint pot. 'You still like dancing?' he asked. She nodded assent. 'Try to come back this way after work tomorrow night. I have still a bit more of the front to paint.'

'I might,' she said teasingly. 'It depends.'

'It depends on what?' he asked anxiously. 'I would come with you as far as the Palace Theatre. We would walk through Soho hand in hand like sweethearts. It's not that I would not like to, but I can't with white paint all over me. You would be ashamed to be seen in my company. A tailor turned painter! By the way, I'll wager you don't even know my name?'

'The only time she mentioned you Daisy called you the younger Bishop boy,' said Julia, laughing, 'but I guessed that you must have a Christian name.'

'It's Richard. Dick if you prefer abbreviations. You will be sure to pass by tomorrow night?'

'I might,' she repeated, 'if it does not rain. Goodbye, Richard.'

She left him with a strange feeling of exhilaration. There were times when it was more fun to talk to a boy than to a girl. She liked him for sticking to his trade. It was the way to succeed these days. But the fact was that as far as information about Daisy was concerned, she had learned nothing. Whether by accident or design he had got the better of her. How much precisely did the Bishop family know? Had the engagement, if there had ever been one, or the involvement, which there obviously was, been stopped by the Bishops because of the case of the postal order at Marlborough Street Police Court? This case, for all Julia knew, might not have been reported in the newspapers. Or was it because Daisy had tried to hasten the marriage by allowing herself to become pregnant, either by neglect or, as some neighbours suggested, on purpose? The first reason, the theft, however trivial, was probably more frightening from the Bishops' point of view than the second. Lots of pregnant girls like Daisy married boys who were still earning insufficient to keep them. Love was known to conquer everything. But how could anybody tell how strong, if at all, their love had been?

With this brief meeting behind her, the evening promised even less than usual. If by some miracle she came upon Daisy's young sister Iris in Old Compton Street they might, of course, decide to brave the wrath of their respective mothers and go dancing in their favourite club off the Tottenham Court Road. But what a to-do it made every time they threw dutifulness to the wind and went off shaking but full of hope to this harmless pastime. Not even alcoholic drinks were served to the members, only lemonade or tepid coffee. On being asked the necessary permission, Julia's mother invariably moaned:

'Well, I suppose so, if it is really your intention to leave me all alone with this splitting headache!' Her pinched lips and her air of martyrdom were calculated to, and actually did, take the edge off Julia's joy at running out to join her friend. For both of the girls the club was, up to now, the most exciting thing in their lives. Well, as it was not likely that Julia would meet Iris tonight in Old Compton Street, or indeed in any other neighbouring street, the solution would probably be to take advantage of what was obviously going to be a dull evening, made even worse by the gaiety of the previous one, to wash and set her hair and to give herself a good manicure. Her hands were small, white, delicate and perfectly shaped, and together with her other physical attractions provided her with a 'dowry' that, if fortune continued to be kind to her, might prove no less valuable than aristocratic birth, allegedly but not actually at a great discount at the present time, or money in the bank.

However, recent conversations worried Julia. Mostly, she was frightened by the ease with which everything could go wrong in an instant. In the case of Edith a gesture of trustfulness, of Daisy a miserable postal order which she had not even needed. There were other things too, and if it were true that troubles came in threes, what would be left of Daisy's youth? Julia reflected that if she herself were to meet this Bishop boy again (she ought really to begin thinking of him as Richard) she must see to it that whatever tender moments they might experience together (though at this stage this was only a dream, a girl's wishful thinking) did not lead her into a maze of lies, bitterness and subterfuge, as appeared so often to be the case with other girls.

When she arrived home, she found her mother standing over the gas stove in an old dressing-gown. Supper was laid on the table. 'We can have supper,' said her mother, 'and then you can make yourself comfortable on the sofa and I will read to you. You were not thinking of going out, I suppose?'

'No,' said Julia. 'I had hoped to go dancing but Iris was nowhere to be seen.'

'We could go to a film if you prefer,' said her mother. 'This new one in Tottenham Court Road is adapted from a novel by one of the Brontës.'

'What is?' asked Julia.

'The film! Why don't you listen?'

'Yes, of course. I am sorry.'

'I read the book aloud to you,' said her mother. 'It is the one that makes you cry.'

Julia cried at plays and films, and even when she saw a stray cat delving into a garbage can. These uncontrollable tears made her feel foolish, and worried her mother who saw in them a sign that her daughter was quite unfitted to face alone the dangers of a fast-moving, scientific world. Julia was evidently not in tune with a modern, sophisticated society in which girls were supposed, in spite of their biological differences, to be the equal of boys. Julia herself found it difficult to believe that she was still terrified of the thought of a mouse under her bed, that she wept at a remembered tune, or that tenderness filled her heart when she saw a London sparrow feeding its fluttering babies on a grimy window ledge in Charing Cross Road and when she heard the love troubles that descended in cascades on many

117

of the girls in the store. Betty, who was so efficient, despised her for this lack of self-control, imagining wrongly that it was affectation, especially when Julia, excusing herself, would disappear with a handkerchief into the Ladies. The Ladies just now was a rendezvous for the young temporary salesgirls hired during the summer season to help deal with holiday makers from the provinces, tourists from the Continent and from America. On Monday mornings, therefore, the temporary staff arrived in the prettiest cheap cotton dresses they had bought over the weekend out of their previous week's pay packet. Julia suffered from her mother's finest qualities. Widowhood made her mother careful with money; she would have blushed with shame to be twenty-four hours late with the rent. The gas bill was paid on time, and there was always a little in the bank. Though a man would have brought home his pay he would have wasted a part of it on sport, tobacco or drink. All men did. Julia's mother had brought up her daughter to admire the genuine and to hate what was sham. Silk, she said, though it was terribly old-fashioned to say so, was better than artificial silk, real lace made in convents or by peasants was more desirable than that made by a machine. Cheap dresses were cheap. One had merely, she said, to examine the seams.

Julia gazed in wonder at the pretty, cheap dresses worn by the temporary staff. She found these girls engaging and, though slightly vulgar, as pretty as butterflies. 'If only I dared break out from the tight lacing of my mother's good taste,' she thought. But habit was strong.

Mrs Davies, she reflected, would have agreed with her mother. They both dressed soberly in clothes cut impeccably out of the best material. Their code of morals was strict. So was Julia's by virtue of her upbringing, but she did sometimes tell herself that it imprisoned a girl in much the same sort of gilded cage as the one which imprisoned the cashier at the store. Her mother's rectitude was for ever holding her back. Though Julia was simply bursting with spontaneity at times, her mother would gently point out that a girl was not supposed to give vent to her joy so inordinately any more than she should make an exhibition of her sorrow. Julia had discovered something else. Edith had been terribly wrong in supposing that Julia's mother would have acted differently from her own. When later, Julia brought the matter up tactfully, her mother made it quite clear that she believed that a lapse forgivable in a really poor girl, without friends or parents, was quite unforgivable in girls like Edith or Daisy who came from comfortable homes and who possessed all the necessities of life.

'If it happened to me,' asked Julia, summoning all her courage, 'would you send me away?'

'I live in the fear that it might happen to you,' said her mother, 'but something tells me that you would have my resilience. We don't go around making a vulgar show of our weaknesses.' Julia tried to puzzle out the exact meaning of her mother's words. What seemed clear was that there existed codes within codes, codes like those of Mrs Davies and Julia's mother which remained intransigent in a world that was getting to accept almost anything without raising an eyebrow.

The worst, thought Julia, would be if nothing happened, nothing at all, if one week followed another without a sign of some tremendous happiness to break the monotony of her life. Her young blood ran hot in her veins. She seldom arrived at the store without a sense of childish amazement at its ever-changing beauty. She had developed the gift of creating for herself a dual personality, that of a docile, hard-working salesgirl and that of a spoilt customer whose adoring husband would stand behind her with an open cheque book. She would start on the first floor, alighting in Edith's department where Edith would show her the prettiest of those model dresses from Paris and New York, then like a bee going from flower to flower pass lightly from department to department collecting shoes with delicate toes and heels, stockings, lingerie, silk squares, gloves, handbags, perfumes with exotic names and every possible exciting new form of make-up, lip-colours from peach-hearted pinks to ripe melon, corals crossed with orange.

The morning proceeded as any other. Towards lunch time Mrs Davies came over to say a few words to the two girls, congratulating them on their work, and then went across to talk with her colleague in the perfumery who could be heard complaining that she was short of competent staff. Being a woman of infinite resource and still young and pretty she had spent most of the morning going from stand to stand helping her girls to serve customers.

On her way out to lunch Julia saw the cashier also leaving the store a few yards ahead and she decided, without too obviously quickening her step, to catch up with her. The slightest degree of hurry was frowned on by the management, and no salesgirl must ever run in case it gave the distressing impression that she was chasing a thief! Fortunately the cashier stopped to look at a handbag, so that Julia had no difficulty in joining her. The price tag of the handbag, cunningly turned round and tucked out of sight, allowed the customer to fall in love with the bag before thinking about the cost. Julia wondered if the cashier really intended to replace the horror she always had seen her with and which, gripped by the handle, beat against her calves as she walked.

'Are you going to buy it? It looks useful,' said Julia encouragingly.

'Hello!' said the cashier, turning round. 'This one? Oh, it's not bad but, between ourselves, I would just as soon change my dear little house in Twickenham as I would my handbag. Getting to know the roominess and weight of a new one wastes so much time. Do you think I could persuade the buyer to keep repeating the same model?'

'You are funny,' said Julia, laughing.

Full of kindness the cashier beamed at her: 'You laugh because you are a vain little thing without a husband or any sort of responsibility,' she said. 'If you were a married woman with children, a house to run and a job like mine, you would think less about your pretty self and be forced to consider how many objects vital to your day's work you could stuff into a useful bag when you left home each morning. I have so many things to worry about.' The cashier took down the bag, opened it, removed the tissue paper which she held lightly above it while peering inside. Then she said: 'Yes, it is a nice bag. The general effect is very pleasing, but I wonder if the clasp is as safe as mine? What do you think? Oh! And what does it matter? I can never make up my mind, even though we can buy things at little more than cost. Do you know what I do? I wait to see if it is still there the next day, and the next day after that. If it disappears, as it is almost certain to do, I am both glad and sorry—sorry to have missed such a pretty bag, delighted that I will not have to think about it any more. You see, Julia, dear, I am very good at figures and can even help the boys with their home-work, but in other ways I'm not at all brave. I just can't spend money on myself!'

'I like listening to you,' said Julia. 'You say such comforting things. From now on I shall keep looking at this corner to see if anybody buys your bag.'

They walked side by side through the store on their way to the main entrance. As they were passing through the perfumery department a young beautician, sent over specially from Paris to launch a new skin cream packed in the most lovely porcelain jars, sang most sweetly but not loud enough to attract attention:

Ah, ce n'était qu'un rêve d'amour
Ah, le joli mensonge d'un jour!

'What a lovely waltz tune,' said the cashier, with a strange, far-away look in her eyes. 'That tune reminds me of when I was a girl. My mother took me to Paris for a week.' She looked at her companion: 'Do you know what the words mean?'

'Something about the love one dreams about not always lasting more than a single day,' said Julia. 'If that happened to me I think I would die!'

4

IN THE street somebody came running up behind her, and before she had time to turn round Edith had put both arms round her, exclaiming: 'Oh, Julia, you would never guess!' The two girls had not seen each other since that evening when they had parted outside the store, each going her own way.

'It's all about that telephone call,' said Edith, falling in step with Julia as they hurried off in the direction of Piccadilly Circus. 'For the moment you must keep it secret. I don't want any of the girls in my department to know, but he did telephone, not once but several times, and now it looks as if it might become serious.'

'Go on!' urged Julia. 'Go on!'

'You remember how I hurried straight back in the hope of finding one of the girls already home? Believe me, I was lucky. I found Agnes changing her dress to go out for the night. "Well?" I asked. "Did he telephone?" "Your new beau?" she said vaguely. "Why, yes, a first time while I was in the bath washing my hair and I wasn't exactly polite to him, dripping water all over the living-room floor and the shampoo not even rinsed out of my hair. A quarter of an hour later when I was under the dryer, he rang again. 'For heaven's sake,' I said, 'what else do you want to know?'" He wanted to know where I was, and Agnes told him that I'd gone out to supper with friends. "What friends?" he asked. "A girl from the store and her mother." "What is the girl's name? Where does she live?" he asked. She told him your name and that you lived alone with your mother somewhere on the fringe of Soho and that she did not expect me back till late. They must have talked for quite a time. In fact, I know they did, and if Agnes had not had that date herself she would certainly have tried to make one with him. Not necessarily to steal him permanently away from me, though it would not be beyond her, but to persuade him to take her to one of the new clubs where she knows very well that most of the men who go there have money to burn.'

'Now I am beginning to understand!' exclaimed Julia. 'What does he look like, your beau?'

'Young, frightfully good looking, serious. He's quite wealthy, the City type who, though he's not a Londoner born, wears a bowler hat and carries a rolled-up umbrella. I'm afraid my beaux run to type. That's what frightens me.'

'Everything makes sense now,' exclaimed Julia. 'Your beau came to the store the next day to buy a diadem for his young niece who lives in Regent's Park and was going to her first important party. Now I know why he said: "You are Julia, I presume?" and "Tell me, Julia, did you have an amusing time last night?"'

'He went to the store,' said Edith, 'mostly to check up that I really had spent the evening with you and with your mother, and not with a boy-friend. He thought that maybe Agnes was covering up for me.'

'So you knew about him coming to the store?'

'He told me at once when we met. In a way you did me a lot of good, unconsciously of course. He said you looked sweet and unspoilt—virginal, that was the word he used, like the heroine in a Victorian novel, and the good impression you made on him rubbed off, so to speak, on me. He added that having checked up once on me he wouldn't need to do it a second time and that he'd convinced himself that I was not the sort of girl to lie. That is what makes me feel so terrible. He comes from my part of the country and supposing, by some malevolent chance, he were to meet Edward, or friends of Edward?'

'How did you meet him?' asked Julia.

'Oh, vaguely,' said Edith. 'Just vaguely. I think it must have been that night I went out dancing with Betty in Leicester Square. He had a car.'

Julia looked sharply at her friend. 'She is lying,' she thought, wanting to scream. 'If she had met him with Betty, then Betty would have recognized him right away. Betty would not have asked me afterwards who he was. He hasn't a face one could easily forget! Edith is lying, and in doing so she has spoilt our relationship. How can I even be sure that she has not lied to me before? How can I ever trust her again?'

'He is staying with a married sister in one of those Nash houses overlooking Regent's Park,' said Edith, ignorant of what was going on in Julia's mind. 'A married sister with two little girls. They have a garden.' The two friends had reached the Café Royal and Edith, suddenly stopping in the middle of the pavement, turned to Julia and said: 'You must pinch me, Julia. I have to make sure I'm not dreaming.' Julia pinched her savagely to revenge herself for the lie. But Edith merely winced and said: 'I won't make the same mistake as I made with Edward. This time it has got to be all or nothing.'

'Did he kiss you?' asked Julia, inquisitive in spite of her annoyance. 'When you met him the next evening—because you did meet him, didn't you? Did he kiss you?'

'No,' confessed Edith. 'Not even after an entire evening together. He drove me home and left me chastely on the doorstep. I had the impression that he was afraid to hurt my feelings. He did not want me to think he was going too fast. He may have thought. . . . Well, that I was too pure! Don't laugh! For heaven's sake, Julia, don't laugh. It's terrible. I feel that I love him already and that I shall never be strong enough to refuse him anything. If he so much as brushes up against my naked arm I literally collapse with tenderness. It's not normal, Julia. People just do not worry any longer about sentiment.'

'I do!' said Julia feelingly.

'I know,' said Edith. 'That is precisely why I value you as a friend. I need your naïveté, your innocence in order that I should not catch myself sleeping with a man just because he takes me out to supper and pays me a compliment. I must harden myself against it. Either I become like the young woman in Maddox Street for whom your mother made that lovely dress who skips profitably from affair to affair, or I remain pure till marriage.' She laughed grimly. 'Oh, I know what you are thinking, but am I so dreadfully wrong to want to start again?'

'No,' said Julia. 'Men do!'

'Youth doesn't last,' said Edith. 'This is my summer. I want to smile up at a warm sun like a rose. Next year it may be too late.' They had reached Piccadilly Circus. Edith waved at the top of the steps leading down into the tube and said: 'Now that I have told you everything, absolutely everything, I must hurry back and change into an evening dress. He is calling for me at eight o'clock. Tonight I must look my best.'

'Well,' thought Julia as her friend disappeared down the stairs. 'What a to-do! Why did she lie to me? What was she trying to hide?' Suddenly she remembered Richard Bishop who presumably would be painting the front of his father's shop at this precise moment. She had promised, or more or less promised, to pass by; but now that she had accompanied Edith as far as Piccadilly Circus, Poland Street was no longer on her way home. In order to pass down it she would have to retrace her steps and make a long, useless detour on high heels when she was tired. Somehow this did not seem honest to her. It would not come strictly under the heading of passing the shop on her way home. Was she sufficiently interested in Richard to do something that had a slight element of dishonesty in it—not to him, not to anybody else but to her own strict principles? Was it not vaguely like Edith's stupid lie?

But it was a fine evening and the slightly longer way home would give her time to reflect quietly on the things that Edith had told her. Turning on her heels she walked briskly through Air Street and Golden Square towards that labyrinth of small streets, grimy houses and colourful street markets that, through daily acquaintance, she had learnt to love, resentful of every modern building that towered above the old houses and menaced their atmosphere and charm. When, after turning in from Broadwick Street, she came in sight of the Bishops' shop, there was no ladder outside and no sign of Richard. The new paint shone brightly in the warm evening air and the door was open, but, because of the frosted glass, she could not see inside. She hesitated, wondering if she dared enter, but, fearing to meet Richard's father and uncertain as to how she could introduce herself, she decided against enquiring for him. She had been childish to suppose that Richard's words had contained anything more than the glib politeness of a boy to a girl.

On reaching home she was surprised and not a little hurt to find the tiny flat empty. Every evening she was so accustomed to finding her mother with a flowered apron round her slim waist, her golden hair piled on top of her pretty head, fussing over the laid supper table that, after the first moment of resentment, panic descended upon her. Had her mother been taken ill? Had an ambulance come to take her away with a clanging of bells? Quickly, with a beating heart, she looked round for a clue then, drawn into the kitchen by an appetizing odour of food, discovered a stew gently bubbling in a pot over a gas ring turned extremely low so that the slightest breath of air would have been enough to extinguish the flame. Julia was relieved. A warm, loving presence was in the house, almost as if her mother were there, without being there. At any rate, Julia decided, there had been no sudden haste in her mother's departure, only a careful determination to see that supper would be ready immediately on her return. She had probably gone to Maddox Street to deliver the finished dress before anything happened to spoil or crease it. Julia lifted the lid again from the pan to sniff appreciatively the appetizing concoction that smelt of herbs and onion. Then, taking off her dress, she put it on a hanger and suspended it against the wide open window of the living-room where it swung gently in the evening breeze. The starlings that started to congregate every night all along Charing Cross Road and across Trafalgar Square, as far as Admiralty Arch, flew low and noisily, the sound of their cries punctuated by the slamming of car doors as the restaurants and theatres filled up. Down in the narrow street she could see a portly Italian waiting like a well-fed spider outside his restaurant. When a taxi came up with guests, he would bow and smile to the women, snapping his fingers for an assistant to bring out a basket from which he would take a posy to be offered to the ladies with a compliment. Lifting her eyes she looked across the low slate roofs with their weather vanes and small red chimney pots. Here and there the sill of an attic window was decorated with geraniums in pots. The light of Piccadilly Circus made a fiery glow in the distance. She tried to remember the words of the old-fashioned waltz sung by the young beautician at the store as she arranged the jars of skin food on her stand: '. . . *rêve d'amour . . . joli mensonge d'un jour!*' Julia hummed it softly, her desire for love—to love and to be loved—wafted over the roofs of Soho . . . Soho where love still flourished, tender plant as it was, in spite of the prostitutes, pimps and basement clubs. So absorbed was she in this dream of a summer evening that, when the door opened sharply behind her, she jumped as if caught doing something wrong. 'Oh, it's you, Mother! Where have you been?' She spoke as an outraged husband might have done if, on returning home from the office, he had found his wife out and the house deserted and had been waiting for her, determined to give her a lesson. Without even putting down her handbag Julia's mother rushed into the kitchen to inspect the pot. 'The buses were all full and the traffic was appalling. I ran. I ran. Are you sure it has not got burnt?'

'No,' said Julia, smiling, once again full of tenderness. 'It smells delicious!'

'I should not have waited for a bus,' said her mother. 'I kept on telling myself there would be room on the next one. In the end I must have stayed there twenty minutes. I should have done better by walking home from the start.' She kicked off the shoes she was wearing and said: 'They are yours. You asked me to break them in for you but I swear you take them a full size too small. These have been killing me.'

Julia picked up her new shoes and looked at them lovingly: 'I will get you your slippers. I am sorry about the shoes, but I love them and you have made them beautifully supple.'

'It doesn't matter,' said her mother. 'I am so glad the stew did not burn. Besides, I have news for you. I had a talk with Daisy's mother!'

Under the strain of what had happened to her daughter, the unfortunate woman had lost several pounds in weight, according to Julia's mother. Daisy was in Paris! Because of her exceptional speed in shorthand and typing she had found herself a situation as private secretary to an executive in the Paris office of a Dutch banking trust. Even Julia's mother had to admit that Daisy had undoubtedly been wise to change her environment in the circumstances. Because of her youth at the time of the affair of the postal order the case against her had been dismissed. Soon it would be entirely forgotten. The Paris experience could only do her good. There remained, however, a much more puzzling aspect to her present situation. She had decided, as indeed it may well have been her intention all along, to keep the child. She was, therefore, some five months pregnant and, according to her mother, Old Madam, who had disappeared from the house at the same time as Daisy, was now living with her in the French capital. What could such curious company portend? At the end of the enlightening conversation, Daisy's mother had invited Julia and her mother to come round for coffee on Sunday afternoon, which would give them the opportunity to meet Iris, who was now working with a wholesale vegetable firm in Covent Garden.

Having served the stew Julia's mother ate with little appetite. She was over-tired and had probably been upset by what she had learnt about Daisy. Julia cleared the table and, having done the washing-up, began tidying the dresser, arranging the cups and saucers, the plates and the cutlery, putting fresh paper on the shelves and in the drawers. Her mother, watching her, found difficulty in controlling her annoyance. The dresser did perhaps need attention, but there was a great deal to do in the flat in spite of its being so small, and her daughter's meddling in a sphere for which she felt herself solely responsible was an open if silent rebuke. She would have liked to tell her sharply to leave what did not concern her and to sit down. There was plenty of sewing she could do. But, on the point of saying this, she reflected that Julia was, to all intent, now a grown woman and that, more important still, she had virtually become more important than she herself was. Without the girl's help she would find it difficult, if not impossible, to live on her dress-making alone, and if she decided out of a desire for prestige to work at some gainful occupation (there was a very modern new blouse factory near the old Royalty Theatre) there would be nobody left at home during the day and this would be tantamount to breaking up their home life altogether.

In the store during the next few days there was a great deal of talk about holidays—in the country, by the sea or abroad. Julia had learnt to make up small bunches of artificial flowers. She invented different combinations and some of them proved popular and gave her the impression of contributing to the department's increasing turnover by something more personal than mere saleswomanship. Thus she put together tiny bunches of poppies, cornflowers and marguerites or ox-eye daisies, which not only reminded her older customers of the days when the English countryside possessed wild flowers in greater profusion than now, especially amongst the growing corn, but the juxtaposition of red, white and blue evoked the wild patriotism that used to surround soldiers marching off to Flanders. She also arranged some bouquets of garden flowers to suggest the English country cottage. The imitation flowers were well made but stiff like soldiers on parade and the green leaves had the smoothness of glass. Born within the sound of the bells of St Martin-in-the-Fields, which in her childhood had

rung out gaily for smart weddings, both in the aristocratic
and the theatrical worlds, Julia dreamt of having a garden.
Her mother talked a great deal about a walled garden in
Sussex, which she (her mother) had known in her girlhood
and in which peaches and nectarines ripened, and where
grew all sorts of other fruit that no longer had the same
sweetness now because there were fewer bees and butterflies. Julia wondered what it would be like to be a rich girl
brought up in the country and taught to ride, which was
every girl's dream. Her mother's client from Maddox Street
had a daughter of about sixteen whose sheltered existence
greatly intrigued Julia. She was called Dorothea, a name
that Julia considered aristocratic, old-fashioned and utterly
delightful. She imagined her, when not riding, as wearing
a flowered dress and a picture hat, possibly of Italian straw
with velvet ribbons, and carrying a parasol as she walked
demurely over well-tended lawns. This was strange in view
of the fact that, as Julia well knew, the client from Maddox
Street's profession was carried on in the purlieus of Bond
Street and Sackville Street, not to speak of Jermyn Street, so
redolent of the poets of Queen Anne's Augustan age. The
extraordinary thing about Julia's mother was that she
combined a natural prudishness and an immense personal
rectitude with an equally wide understanding and sympathy
with the difficulties and problems of other women, especially
those who had not been favoured with money or social
position in their youth. One felt that Julia's mother had
experienced all the many poignant problems that a woman
could be called upon to face, and though there was, without
question, an embittered side to her character there was also
this extraordinary mixture of compassion and insatiable
inquisitiveness that had caused her to become a much
sought-after repository of feminine gossip and secrets.
This gossip she willingly shared with Julia, and though she
might have hesitated to send her daughter round to
Maddox Street with a dress, she never tried to hide from
Julia the nature of her client's profession or the strange and
wonderful stories connected with it that were revealed to

her, and by many others besides, during those long fittings that took place over a cup of strong tea in the Soho flat while Julia was at the store making up her posies of artificial flowers.

Edith had developed a habit of telling Julia that she was naïve and far too innocent, but this was not an accurate reading of her friend's character. Julia was not a bit naïve. She was naturally pure and sentimental. Her emotions and tears were genuine. When her mother recounted to her the gossip of those women for whom she made such beautiful dresses, there was not an atom of selfconsciousness on the part of one or the other. Their amusement had no vice in it and Julia never ceased for her part to dream of pure love. 'And this,' insisted her mother, 'was still the dream of most girls.' Though there were periods when a society was over-tolerant in the abstract, it remained just as prudish in the particular. Had not Edith discovered that to her cost? Nor was there any point in closing one's eyes to the world about one. Why should she refuse to make a dress for such a warm-hearted client as this elegant woman from Maddox Street?

One had to admit also that the client from Maddox Street was infinitely more aware than most allegedly honest women of how a young girl like Julia should be treated. No bad word would have ever fallen from her lips. Though she was probably aware that Julia's mother had no secrets from her daughter, she herself would not for the world have mentioned her profession, or anything to do with it, to Julia. She treated Julia as an Edwardian mother in the best society would have treated her children, with consideration and respect. For this reason Julia loved to see her tripping quickly across the crowded store to bid her good morning, often to present her with some small but pretty thing she had chosen on the way.

No doubt this positive need for propriety did lead to some strange situations, but not more so than was quite frequent amongst the profession. If Julia's mother had never asked her daughter to deliver a dress or a message to her client in

Maddox Street, it was due to a great extent to her unwillingness to disturb a person at her office. Because the flat in Maddox Street was to its owner what a doctor's consulting room is to a doctor or a solicitor's office to a solicitor. In principle it was used solely during office hours, which in the case of the client from Maddox Street could be from early afternoon till midnight. Every Friday she went to her beautifully appointed home in Marble Arch where, like any other successful business woman, she lived a life of leisure, and when Dorothea came for weekends she even put on her prettiest house-coat and went down to the kitchen to help make the porridge for breakfast.

Nevertheless, as Julia's mother was a great deal more down to earth than might at first be thought, and hard, even cruel, on occasion, so one must not suppose that her client from Maddox Street was a vain, vaporous blonde. Her pretty head was tightly screwed to her shoulders. She owned not merely the flat in Maddox Street but the house itself. It was pure Georgian and had become a most valuable property. She read the *Financial Times* and knew about old silver, and was so little in the clouds that she once said to Julia's mother: 'I have sent Dorothea to one of the best schools. The former seat of a great English family built in the eighteenth century and standing in more than one hundred acres of parkland and woods. It is two hundred, or perhaps three hundred, feet above sea level. They own their own stables, their own riding horses, their own lawn tennis courts. I went down to see it for myself. There are science laboratories, libraries, domestic science rooms and a great hall with antlers and portraits of ancestors. They teach them Latin, Greek, pianoforte and elocution. And now I can guess what you are going to ask me. Does she know? Well, of course, it's a problem but I have learnt to be patient. She knows? She doesn't know? She guesses? She does not guess? What do I do in the circumstances? I say nothing and I get on with my job. My job is to give her what she would never have had otherwise. That is the only form of honesty I am aware of. I give her everything she asks for. When she wants to go with a wealthy girl friend to St Tropez, I give her the wherewithal to cut as good a figure as any girl on earth. I love her, but I have no illusions about my capabilities. The profession I belong to is the only one in which I could earn a living. Could I marry again? You know as well as I do that no worth-while man would marry me. The rules today are the same as they have always been. Nothing fundamental ever changes.'

'What about the future? Dorothea's future?'

'Every one of her birthdays brings the nightmare nearer,' said the woman from Maddox Street. 'One must believe in one's guiding star.'

The part about Dorothea's school, the stables and the horses, the piano lessons and the holidays at St Tropez made no impression at all on Julia's mother, who merely saw in her client a woman who, when still young, had been deserted by a man and left to bring up a baby girl without adequate resources. Once when mother and daughter had watched her slim and pretty figure walking away from a fitting down their rather squalid street, Julia's mother had said, peering behind the lace curtain of the living-room window: 'You know, she looks so certain of herself! How could anybody guess that she is obliged to go through life balancing herself on a tight-rope!'

'Dorothea, at all events,' said Julia, 'has everything.'

'Yes,' agreed her mother, 'everything except a father.'

'I suppose it was hard luck when her mother was deserted by her father to have been left with her—with a baby, I mean?' Julia added, looking up rather nervously at her mother.

'The child is all she lives for,' said Julia's mother. 'Only yesterday she said to me: "Before it was born I tried to get rid of it. Today Dorothea is everything I love best in the world. If I lost her I would die."'

Julia reflected that her mother's client was fortunate in one respect, to have found herself, at the time of her desertion, with a baby girl and not a baby boy to bring up. In the profession she had chosen, a boy, as he grew strong, independent, critical, enquiring, would, she supposed, have been even more embarrassing. Dorothea, Julia's mother had told her, was now a truly beautiful girl, the very image of what her mother must have looked like at her age. When she had gone with those wealthy school friends to St Tropez she had made a positive sensation. Few girls had as many dates, as many escorts. 'But,' said Julia's mother to Dorothea's mother, 'with everything that you know from your profession about the duplicity and faithlessness of men, are you not terrified for your daughter?'

'Oh, no!' said Dorothea's mother with staggering ingenuousness. 'There must be a few good ones, and I am relying on her to fall for one of them!'

There would be no St Tropez for Julia of course. Holidays in her mother's opinion did not fall into the category of necessities, except on doctor's orders to recuperate from some unusually severe illness. No vacation, especially with the London parks so agreeable on summer evenings, would justify jeopardizing their slender savings. Though Julia pushed the thought out of her mind, a revolt of youth, eager for excitement, eager for love, surged through her. Her friend Edith, always exotically beautiful, had become radiant and only the other day Julia had seen her wearing an original model from one of the great Paris *couture* houses. There was no doubt that as she rose in importance in her department so she was gaining poise and assurance. The opinion she expressed about her buyer had been considerably modified. They still addressed each other coldly but with growing politeness. Her buyer had become the Chief who needed to be strongly seconded. 'I still intend to eat her up,' said Edith, 'but not too quickly. I need to learn from her everything she knows. This dress I am wearing was hers. She got it during her last business trip to Paris. I bought it from her at her own price which was probably more than she paid for it. My victory was twofold. I have a dress that adds to my prestige and my personality, and I have put her in my debt to a certain extent. So you see, I may not be in her shoes yet, but I am in her dress and when I am ready to strike, I shall win.' Edith, of course, had already taken her holidays, though she was now almost unrecognizable as the Edith who had set off modestly by Channel steamer to Ostend. She now planned a weekend in Paris, doubtless as a foretaste of what it would be like when she would go there, as she felt certain she would, as a buyer, to attend the winter or spring collections. What would she find to do all alone during a short weekend? Well, at least she could walk past the famous display windows of the great stores behind the Opéra, saunter down the Rue St Honoré, and come back early on Monday morning to talk about what she had seen. Perhaps this would impress even the young man who now was calling for her almost every evening to take her to theatrical first nights and fashionable restaurants.

Julia had made a date with Iris to go dancing with her at the small club off the Tottenham Court Road. They had arranged everything in advance with their respective mothers. There would be no recriminations.

They set off in high spirits along Tottenham Court Road, beyond Oxford Street which with its incessant traffic ran like a mighty river between their world—the world of Soho and Regent Street, St Martin's Lane and Covent Garden, so familiar to them, so loved in its every mood—and a region of a quite different atmosphere, belonging almost to another city, of Rathbone Place with its rag trade, Percy Street with its continental-style restaurants, and the frightening approaches to the Middlesex Hospital with its wards, its nurses' home, its clanging ambulance bells and its doctors in white coats. The club was an almost family affair originally started by a number of young medical students and their colleagues from London University. Daisy had discovered it first and when, as an act of condescension, she took her sister Iris and Julia along, the two younger girls often remained partnerless at their table while Daisy, three years their senior, sophisticated, sure of herself, stunning in a new dress and the very latest hair style, was seized upon by the best dancer in the room.

Tonight as they walked into the club, rather too early and slightly selfconscious, the thought of Daisy, never once mentioned, came uncomfortably between them. Julia would not have dared to ask Iris what news, if any, the family had received from Paris. An air of mystery had descended over the house, was interpreted in different ways by the neighbours, intrigued the entire district, and Iris had not come to the club to speak about something that vaguely frightened her. She had come to have a good time and to dance. Julia, too, had been looking forward to the evening, which was perhaps the nearest she would get to a summer vacation.

Her mother had made her for the occasion a superb dress in a finely pleated material that swirled out every time she swung round on her heels and gracefully subsided to pencil slimness as soon as she stood still. Iris also had a lovely dress. 'Do you recognize it?' she asked almost aggressively. 'It was Daisy's, but Daisy will not know about it because Daisy is no longer here. I shall not have to share a room with her any more and I can borrow all her prettiest dresses. This is the one I like best.'

Iris had suddenly become old enough to become a secretary herself. Her job in Covent Garden gave her the same prestige as Daisy had enjoyed when she was a secretary in the General Office at the store. She carried her head so high that almost immediately she was invited by a medical student to dance, and when she returned to the table where Julia, inwardly vexed, had been sitting out, she said with false sympathy:

'My poor Julia, it looks as if the new dress your mother made you is not going to prove a lucky one!'

'Oh, please don't say that!' said Julia miserably. 'I felt so happy in it and you yourself said that it was beautiful.'

'That, alas, has nothing to do with it,' said Iris. 'A dress is either lucky or unlucky. Everybody knows that. Some bring one happiness from the word go; others are best left hanging at the back of the wardrobe. This dress of Daisy's, for instance, invariably brought her an immediate invitation to dance. In fact, men looked at her the moment she entered the club. That is why I decided to borrow it this evening, and, as you see, I was right. We scarcely had time to sit down before I was chosen. Whereas you, my poor Julia, in spite of your new dress, are still here, trying not to look disappointed.'

'We have only just arrived,' said Julia, telling herself that if she was obliged to sit out much longer the pleats of her dress would lose their shape at the back. Fortunately all the evening stretched before them. Anything could happen. There were still, at this stage of the proceedings, far more girls than men. The girls always arrived on time, afraid to miss a single dance. The men knew very well that as soon as they appeared they could pick on any girl they pleased.

Iris said suddenly:

'If only Daisy would never return home! It is terrible to go through life being made to feel that one is the younger sister. Just because she was three years older and brought a pay packet home, she thought she could give me orders. I had to make her bed in the morning and wash and iron her slips and nightdresses. Most of my clothes were left-overs from her wardrobe. Now that she has gone I shall be the one to bring a pay packet home and all her lovely clothes will be mine. I tell you, I hope she never comes back!'

Still smarting under her friend's remarks about her new dress, Julia said:

'You'll see. Daisy will come back. She is so much prettier and more capable than we are!'

Now it was Julia's turn to be chosen. A young laboratory assistant, with whom she had previously danced at the club, came over to ask her. He was a nice boy, unassuming, and of no particular importance, as far as she was aware, but he had cool, dry hands, was light on his feet and had a good sense of rhythm. These last qualities made him a much appreciated partner. As she turned and twisted, happiness returned to her. After a while Iris, who had not been asked to dance this time, and who was going through an agony of shame to be seen sitting out, got up and walked defiantly with a rather flushed face to the cloakroom, leaving Julia's handbag unguarded on the table. This worried Julia because the club was beginning to fill up and she would not be able to keep a satisfactory eye on it. Girls were requested to leave their handbags with the attendant, and some of them did so, but afterwards they were apt to feel stupid as they selfconsciously walked about wondering what to do with their hands. It was like trying to sew without a thimble. One felt quite lost. For this reason it was an accepted thing that when several girls were at the same table none would walk off while the others were dancing and leave their handbags unattended. Once again Julia felt let down by her friend who, she felt sure, was trying to spoil her evening. Now Iris had returned and was talking to a boy who seemed vaguely familiar. The boy turned his head towards the dance floor and Julia recognized Richard Bishop. Iris had become animated. She was arching her neck and trying to appear sophisticated. With Daisy's dress on her back, was she trying to seduce Daisy's first boy-friend? Because Daisy had gone out quite often with Richard before deciding to concentrate on the more ambitious brother whom she had certainly hoped to trap into marriage. There was something sinister in the younger sister's desire to step inside the elder sister's skin.

The laboratory assistant accompanied Julia back to her table where Iris had just arrived with Richard. 'Hello!' said Richard, looking at her roguishly.

'What am I supposed to say?' asked Julia, pirouetting in her new dress as a sign of defiance at Iris. 'What happened to your ladder and paint brush the other evening? Didn't we arrange to meet?'

'You never told me you knew Julia!' Iris exclaimed angrily. 'Is it true you even date her?'

'I date every pretty girl I see,' said Richard. 'Come on, Julia. Let us dance!'

While they were dancing, he said:

'I'm sorry about the other night. I loved seeing you. I really did. Not only that, you brought me luck, the most incredible piece of luck I've ever had. The morning after I saw you, I got a message from one of the most important firms in the West End asking me to join them as a cutter. My father was mad with pride. As for me, I can think of nothing else. This is my first free moment. I wanted to celebrate, and I had a faint idea that I might find you here. You looked so much more interested than most girls the other evening when I talked to you about my work and my ambitions. You are the sort of girl a man wants to talk to about his business aspirations.'

Julia smiled up at him.

'I would be glad for you to make money,' she said. 'There would not be much in a man who did not dream of making a success of his life. Every profession is good at the top. At least you know what you want. For a girl, for a girl like myself, that makes you interesting.'

He looked down at her:

'What a funny little thing you are!' he said. 'So much sense behind that golden hair. Are you sure you don't look down on me for wanting to be a ladies' tailor?'

'So was Worth,' said Julia. 'So also was Paul Poiret. They, and many others, managed to live like figures out of the Arabian Nights. Town houses. Country estates. Old Masters. Impressionists. Champagne parties on houseboats moored to the quays of the Seine like the houseboats on the Isis at Oxford. What have you to be ashamed of?'

'I never thought of it that way,' he said. 'Who told you?'

'About the champagne? I read it in a book.'

He laughed.

'Now you really are being a scatterbrained girl,' he said. 'Let me tell you about the head cutter—a Rumanian, born in Liverpool, a true artist but a balding man who suffers atrociously from stomach ulcers. He treats me as an enemy. Why? Because I am younger than he is and have no ulcers. He knows that the firm has engaged me in order to replace him when he retires next year. So he hates me and I don't blame him. On the other hand, he goes out of his way to teach me all his secrets. This mixture of hate and paternal affection bewilders me. All this is a long way from champagne parties on the Seine.'

'You dance very well,' said Julia. 'Is that something else they taught you in Rome?'

'Young Romans taught me how to grasp a girl firmly round the waist. So! Holding her like this, in the small of her back, so that she bends like a reed gracefully. They call it a prelude to the first kiss. Dancing is a dangerous pastime for pretty girls in Rome.'

'I'll take that risk,' said Julia, laughing. 'Out of gratitude because you do not step on my toes.'

They danced silently for a while, each lost in a warm, pleasant, enveloping reverie. Seated alone at their table, Iris looked with an almost sad smile at Richard and Julia, wondering if they had fallen in love. This development was taking her by surprise. Richard's brother Alan, a mysterious figure, alleged to be the creator of Daisy's troubles but apparently unaware of the sensation he caused amongst inhabitants of the narrow streets between Seven Dials and Soho Square, was dancing with a pale, flat-chested girl quite devoid, thought Iris, of charm. Had Alan come to the club with his brother? Was he aware of Iris's presence? Iris was beginning to wonder if perhaps it was more difficult than she had supposed to step inside the skin of her glamorous, if unfortunate, elder sister. This sudden deterioration in her affairs might be a punishment of course for exhibiting herself in Daisy's dress. A dress that Daisy considered lucky might not necessarily prove lucky to another girl, especially to a younger sister. It might even be trying, if a dress had a soul, to revenge itself for having been stolen. Daisy had once given Iris a cast-off green dress that had certainly done her no good. Indeed, though Iris had altered the sleeves and the bodice, she had ended by believing that Daisy had cast a spell over it. Iris refused ever to wear green again. She even put her jade necklace in her handbag and, while crossing over Waterloo Bridge, took it out and cast it into the Thames.

She might have been wrong, she thought, even to allow herself to be sent to that school to learn to become as proficient as Daisy in shorthand and typing. Here again she had been forced to follow in her elder sister's footsteps. Her own private dream had been to be a ballet dancer, but one had to start young, and her parents, her father specially, had objected. She tried to console herself by reflecting that very few girls succeeded in ballet and they earned very little when they did. Perhaps Julia had not done so badly for herself by becoming a salesgirl in a Regent Street store. She might even end up as a career girl. Meanwhile she could watch the changing faces of the customers; at least she did not have to stay in an office all day.

Escorted back to the table, Julia sat down beside her friend while Richard, with a cheery smile to both of them, went off, perhaps to choose another girl. Like a child who'd been too long at a party, Julia yawned. She had enjoyed dancing with the rather grave young man who talked so knowingly about his art, but now she was tired and wished that she were already in bed with her novel and the sound of her mother's voice in the adjoining room asking all about her evening. Julia also wanted some advice about the dress she should wear in the morning. Mrs Davies had summoned her to one of those routine interviews that had done so much to mark Julia's progress at the store. Edith had told her that in her dealings with her buyer she should be neat but not aggressively conspicuous. Her hem line especially should not be too short.

'Let's go home!' she said, turning to Iris.

'Already?' said Iris, not willing openly to admit that she too was tired of the evening. 'There are at least four more dances. One never knows what can happen.'

Julia said nothing.

'Besides,' said Iris, 'you haven't done so badly. Richard is a nice boy.'

Julia shrugged her shoulders.

'Yes,' she conceded without enthusiasm. 'He's a nice boy.'

After another small silence, Iris asked:

'Did he mention Daisy?'

Julia blushed.

141

'Daisy? Why on earth should he mention Daisy? No, of course not. He never once mentioned her.'

Julia's hairline was still pink. Though she had told Iris the truth, the absolute truth, she gave every appearance of having lied. She had lied in a way. That other evening when Richard came down the ladder with his paint pot to greet her, there had been a brief reference to the involvement, and ever since this had hung like a little cloud between them.

Iris pinched her brightly painted lips and Julia, looking at her, thought: 'What little cannibals we are!' But though they were ready to devour each other, each needed the other's company. Both were, in fact, very near to tears. Their evening had brought them precisely nothing.

But there was always tomorrow, thought Julia, as a bespectacled young student came over to ask Iris to dance. Julia watched them disappear with a sense of gratitude. Iris would regain her poise and assurance. Their return home would be less melancholy, less full of mutual recrimination. 'Yes,' she thought, reverting to her hopes for the morrow, 'Edith may have something amusing to tell me.' Edith had asked Julia to come round to the flat one evening when the other two girls with whom she shared it were likely to be at home. They would all have dinner together and discuss one another's problems. Such an experience would give Julia the impression of being emancipated. It was not good for her continually to be with her mother, as if she were not old enough to live on her own.

Because Iris was convinced that her luck had changed for the better, the two girls decided to postpone their departure, and soon afterwards Julia found herself chosen twice running by a young man who had just come down from Oxford. He filled her romantic mind with descriptions of afternoons spent punting on the Cherwell, or reading and dreaming on the banks where the meadows, golden with buttercups, pungent with the scent of white and red hawthorn, ran down to the river's edge. 'How vividly he evokes what I shall never know,' she thought with a touch of sadness. She remembered what Edith had once said to her about Edward who had brought her so much unhappiness and yet so much joy. She had loved him because he had the aura of intellectual as well as actual wealth. The assurance of several generations of success and learning was his. 'You know, Julia,' she had said to her friend, 'by forming my taste, he rendered me incapable of finding satisfaction in less intelligent men. This was perhaps the greatest disservice he rendered me!'

'I think you are wrong,' said Julia. 'Nothing one learns need be wasted.'

Towards the end of the second dance Julia, shaking her golden hair from her eyes, looked up at her companion and asked:

'Are you going to be a doctor?'

'Why do you ask?'

'Most of the men who come to the club are medical students or at least have some connection with the Middlesex Hospital.'

He laughed.

'Well, answer me,' she said, annoyed. 'Are you going to be a doctor?'

'Not exactly,' he said.

'What do you mean by not exactly? I suppose you are in some sort of research?'

'No,' he answered. 'You are too inquisitive. As a matter of fact my family are undertakers.'

'Oh!' she exclaimed. 'How terrible!'

Now she was covered with confusion, but when all young men looked more or less the same it did seem difficult for a girl like Julia not to react spontaneously and lay herself open to such surprises. Her partner merely laughed at her rudeness. As far as he was concerned she was just an amusing, not very well educated, fluffy little thing he had picked on for the last two dances at a cellar club. She was light as a feather, nice to hold, and her teeth, when she looked up and laughed, were like pearls. Her golden hair smelt of some rather expensive French perfume and her waist was so slim that it was a pleasure to encircle. She would be well worth dating for supper one night and bringing back to his bachelor flat, or maybe going round to hers.

'You live near here?' he asked.

Feeling very small in his arms, the top of her head against his cheek, she had the uncomfortable impression of being in a warm, snug coffin. 'I wish he had not told me,' she thought. This was always happening to girls who went once or twice a week to clubs or dance halls. As Edith said, 'just one more wasted evening'.

'I am tired,' she said. 'I think I have danced too much.'

'You haven't told me where you live,' he said. 'Do you and that other girl live together?'

'No,' she said.

'Come on!' he said. 'Where is your flat?'

'On the fringe of Soho,' she said.

He looked pleased. The location appeared to confirm his suspicions. The music stopped. She turned sharply on her heels, and began to walk back to her table.

'Wait!' he whispered into her shoulder. 'Can't I come round?'

'No,' she said. 'Mother will be waiting up for me.'

In fact, after bidding Iris good night at the corner of their street, Julia found her mother already in bed.

'Did you girls enjoy yourselves?' her mother asked, getting up and pouring milk into a pan to make her daughter some hot chocolate.

'Not particularly,' said Julia. 'Iris was a real cat and I danced with an undertaker.'

'You will both end by being murdered,' said her mother. 'Who else did you see?'

'The two Bishop boys were there. I danced with the one Daisy was not engaged to. He is going to be a cutter like his father.'

'He is too young,' said her mother. 'He could not keep you and there is no telling if he will make the grade.'

'I know,' said Julia, pulling off her stockings. 'They are either too young or they are married—and the rest are policemen or undertakers.'

She took the cup of steaming hot chocolate from her mother and asked:

'Was it like that when you were a girl?'

'It is always like that,' said her mother. 'What makes me feel guilty, as far as you are concerned, are the few opportunities you have to meet really nice boys. A store like the one you work in is not unlike being in a girls' school. The buyers as well as all the employees are women. Oh, I know it is fun and the chances of advancement are often better. Then also you have more liberty after work than girls had in my day. You can do pretty well as you like.'

The slight edge in her mother's voice on reaching these last few words rang a warning bell. Julia put the cup of chocolate on her bedside table, and opening her wardrobe took out a hanger on which to suspend her new dress. Then she threw her arms round her mother's neck, saying:

'My lovely, lovely dress had a wonderful time and I love it more and more!'

Her mother smiled.

'Tell me about the pleats,' she said. 'Did they swirl when you danced?'

Mrs Davies was seated as usual behind her table. On it today stood a tall vase containing an immense bunch of sweet-smelling lavender that seemed to impart a mauve heat haze to the little room. She had brought it from her own garden. Having inspected Julia, she said:

'You wear the prettiest dresses, Julia. I am quite jealous of you. Please convey my respects to your clever mother!'

'Thank you!' said Julia, blushing.

'I have already seen Betty,' said Mrs Davies, 'to tell her that I'm going for a short holiday. I have decided not to have anybody replace me during my absence. Temporary buyers are prone to show an excess of zeal and to make unnecessary changes that affect sales adversely. If you and

Betty can work happily together, as I'm sure you can, that is all I need.'

'Be assured of that, Madam,' said Julia.

'Personally I would gladly do without a holiday,' said Mrs Davies. 'I travel sufficiently in the course of the year, but my husband has had an anxious time in the City, and as he's bought himself a new car he wants to take me to the south of Spain. I fear it will be very hot.'

Julia, with her eyes fixed attentively on Mrs Davies's features, decided that her chief looked tired. It had not struck her until then that this woman, whom she admired so greatly, could age or could have any but the most minor problems. Julia's problems and those of her mother consisted to a great extent of how far they could make every penny stretch. In calculating the yardage for a dress or for a skirt her mother habitually cut it so fine that when she brought the material home and started making the garment she was nearly always obliged, at the last moment, to perform some miracle of invention not to have to go running back to the shop for another quarter of a yard. Laughingly, she used to say that the secret of making a really stunning dress was to start off with an insufficiency of material!

But Mrs Davies had no such problems. She was a successful career woman with a clever husband. She owned, in addition to the husband, all sorts of things that at the present at least were further from Julia's world than the moon was from our own—to wit, a house with a garden, a maid, a new motor-car and (Julia's mother would have added) a wardrobe with a built-in mirror. Curiously enough, this last object was the one thing in the world that Julia's mother most desired and for some obscure reason had never possessed. On what she earned from dressmaking and from what Julia earned at the store, it seemed most unlikely that this wish would be fulfilled in the near future.

All this proved how difficult it was for Julia to imagine that Mrs Davies could ever grow older. Yet small blue veins were visible on her hands, and she did definitely

146

appear tired, almost as tired as Julia's mother. How long
had Julia known her? Julia had arrived at the store early the
previous autumn. Soon she would have been there a full
year.

Mrs Davies rose. The interview was ended.

'Goodbye, Julia,' she said. 'Give my love to Betty. I
must bring you both some small gift from my travels.
Which would you prefer, Julia, some perfume or a handbag?'

As Julia passed through the restaurant on her way to the
stairs, the young waitresses with their pretty lace caps and
pink organdie aprons stood waiting for the first customers.
Several knew Julia from having frequently met her in the
Ladies and they smiled at her as she passed: 'Hello, Julia!
Been to see your boss, dear? Good luck, Julia!'

The buyers had the right, if not the obligation, to lunch
in the customers' gay, beautifully feminine restaurant. They
had a special discount but were judged by the waitresses by
their generosity in tips. Edith, who had no sort of doubt at
all that she would soon be a buyer, had already in imagination chosen her table. It was to be by the huge plate glass
window so that she could peer down into the traffic of
Regent Street. 'On rainy days,' she had said to Julia, 'I shall
be able to reflect how fortunate I am to be lunching in this
elegant restaurant instead of getting my shoes soaked
queueing up outside some coffee bar.'

Julia, on the other hand, was merely anxious to keep her
job. Mrs Davies was kind to her but this did not necessarily
mean very much. It was not that Julia lacked ambition, but
it was not quite the same sort of ambition. She constantly
dreamt of a larger flat with a modern kitchen and a luxurious
bathroom. She wanted them as much for her mother as for
herself. Her mother, at Julia's age, had also been pretty. If
one could judge by faded photographs, taking into account
the difference in hair styles and clothes, her mother had been
exceptionally pretty with that beautiful golden hair that
Julia had inherited from her, the well-rounded bust, the
very slim waist, the long, perfectly shaped legs—and those
tiny hands and perfect teeth. She should have had the world

at her feet of course, but that never happened. Nobody, until Julia grew up, had appeared adequately to appreciate her immense qualities—her beauty, her good sense, her infinite capacity for hard work and making do on practically no money, and her innate good taste. This was perhaps the most remarkable of her qualities, the one that transcended everything and was never blunted but, on the contrary, burned fiercely right through her adversity. She had also surprised her daughter by the diversity of her knowledge, which ranged from such small feminine accomplishments as sewing, embroidering, knitting and ironing, to an unusual grasp of those English novels that had charmed her forebears in Victorian and Edwardian days but that were now practically forgotten by all those who had not inherited a pile of old books in an attic.

For all these reasons Julia felt that she was destined for a future that would erase to some extent the misfortunes that had so persistently dogged her mother. What Julia now suffered from was her mother's exaggerated modesty, that modesty which Edith was always falsely interpreting as naïveté. Julia's mother had some reason to be modest. When nothing one does, when no quality one possesses, is ever appreciated, how can one be other than modest? However, Julia was not entirely modest in not wanting to throw her weight about with her buyer. She would not have known how to set about it. If there was anything that worried her just now it was that after nearly a year at the store, though life in all its aspects continued to excite and interest her, she felt that perhaps something important was late in arriving. And this something important, she felt, was a great deal more than becoming a buyer in a store.

When she got home that evening her mother had what her daughter called her look of past or impending doom. Some client had probably complained about a dress, or had haggled over the bill. If only they knew what sweated labour they encouraged! There were many misconceptions of modern life, thought Julia. First amongst these was that semi-skilled workers earned a great deal too much money;

secondly, that daughters no longer respected their mothers. No daughter in any age could have held her mother in greater respect than Julia held hers. Any small slight against her drove her mad.

'Hello,' she said, picking up a huge box of broken chocolates. 'I see that Miss Pauline has been here. She is sweet to bring us all these broken chocolates—even if they're not sufficiently presentable to sell.'

'There are some *marrons glacés* underneath,' said her mother greedily.

Julia's mother liked sweet things, and sugared chestnuts were her particular delight.

'How is Miss Pauline?' asked Julie.

This slim, angular woman was no longer young, but she liked to boast that her gentleman friend was madly in love with her. He would, she said laughing, do absolutely anything (except divorce his wife) to please her, and she invariably accompanied this remark with a wink, both theatrical and vulgar, but evoking great hidden sensuousness.

'She came to choose two tweed skirts and a new autumn dress,' said Julia's mother. 'After it was all over, her gentleman friend came to fetch her. Actually he stood below the open window and called up, and so Miss Pauline leaned out in her slip when she heard him and told him that she was coming down right away. Really, she was radiant, and as soon as she was dressed, flew down the stairs to meet the wicked man.'

Was this something that had shocked Julia's mother? A little, perhaps. Miss Pauline's goings on with a married man who used the window as if it were a stage set out of a Shakespearian play was not exactly inspiring to the neighbours in the street, but then again, thought Julia, her mother might have been a tiny bit jealous. Love occasionally inspires love or conversely makes one uncomfortably aware of the lack of it. Miss Pauline, of course, had a certain contempt for her clever dressmaker to whom she would say, even if Julia were in the room:

'You are plain idiotic, a young and attractive widow like

you, to spend the best years of your life with your mouth full of pins, kneeling at the feet of other women to make them beautiful!'

Julia's mother would wince. This was always an awkward moment. Especially as both mother and daughter knew that if Julia was there, she also would be told with affectionate virulence: 'As for you, Julia, why are you not out and about with some nice young man instead of wasting your time here at home with your mother?'

The sombre look that Julia had noticed in her mother's features was not, however, the result either of any remark by Miss Pauline or of her strange behaviour. There was a very different reason for it. She said:

'As I was passing Daisy's house this evening on my way back from the baker's I heard voices behind the half-open front door. There seemed a very familiar tone about them, so I stopped to fiddle with my handbag, pretending to search for my own front door key. Almost immediately Daisy's door was opened from the inside, and what do you suppose I saw? Believe it or not, out came Old Madam wearing a black hat trimmed with red and our Daisy leaning heavily on a stick!'

'I thought she was in Paris!' exclaimed Julia.

'Her ankles were quite swollen,' said her mother, 'and she appeared to be in considerable pain.'

'Could she have had her baby?' asked Julia, beginning to count the months on her fingers, and arriving at the obvious conclusion that, as the affair of the postal order had already taken place eight months ago, just before Christmas to be exact, and that as Daisy's involvement with the Bishop boy had clearly been prior to that, there could indeed have been plenty of time for Daisy to have had her baby.

'Did they see you?' asked Julia.

'No,' said her mother. 'Old Madam was holding Daisy's left arm and they turned immediately the other way.'

'Why should Daisy's ankles be so swollen?' asked Julia, already aware of what her mother would answer. But though in certain circumstances it might happen to any woman after giving birth, there might also have been some measure of hereditary weakness on her mother's side in Daisy's case. Daisy's mother was one of those stout, slow-moving women with a crown of fair hair, the colour of ripe corn, and large, appealing, almost babyish blue eyes. For as long as Julia or Julia's mother could remember, she had suffered from a weakness in her short swollen legs. She had worked too hard, done too much standing, piling the family wash into the old-fashioned copper in the yard, hanging the wet linen up on the line, and cooking those stupendous Sunday lunches on the gas rings in the basement. Julia's thoughts had flown to Iris. She imagined her panic at the sudden return of the prodigal elder sister who would quickly discover the rape of her wardrobe and the attempted usurpation of her place in the family. 'Iris was right,' thought Julia, recalling her words at the dance club. 'Some dresses do bring bad luck. She would have done better not to steal Daisy's.'

Julia's mother, dismissing the subject, said brightly:

'Let's go to the pictures. I have had a long, tiresome day and feel like escaping into a different world—a world beyond the end of our street. If the film disappoints us, we could have an ice at the Corner House or go for a stroll in Green Park.'

Julia, who had worn high-heeled shoes all day, would have preferred not to continue the agony of those piercing stabs. She must be prudent, however. Were she to say: 'No, please, Mother. I can't tell you how my corn hurts!' her mother might be justified in answering: 'I notice you never mention your corn when you want to go dancing with a girl-friend!'

She said, forcing a smile:

'I'll put on some shoes with low heels. After all, we aren't likely to meet anybody!'

It was one of those hot evenings in August when the London air becomes clogged with particles of dust, when scraps of paper are strewn over the pavements, and when huge ochre-fleshed peaches from Italy, so different from the beautiful English variety, overflow from barrows at every street corner. As Julia and her mother crossed Cambridge Circus a fire-engine came out of the fire station at the bottom of Shaftesbury Avenue, its crew still pulling on their coats and adjusting their helmets, bells clanging as it clattered across the road on its way into Tottenham Court Road. A policeman held out an arm to allow it to cross on the wrong side of the Circus. Another smaller vehicle with a more modest bell followed it, and a moment later all returned to normal.

Taking the north side of Shaftesbury Avenue Julia and her mother mingled with a crowd that more than ever at this time of year was picturesquely cosmopolitan. One heard many different languages, and saw a great variety of dress. Julia thought that Mrs Davies could have travelled equally well without leaving the West End. She slipped an arm through her mother's and, in doing so, became aware that her mother had become thinner, almost skinny. It had seemed to her that only a few months back her mother's arms were rounder and plumper. Overcome by tenderness, she squeezed her mother's wrist gently, and had she dared she would have kissed her right in the middle of Shaftesbury Avenue. Her mother had stopped to look at a dress in the window of a shop. She had been intrigued by the cut of the sleeves and by the way the hem had not been ironed flat. This was how her mother kept in close touch with the vagaries of swiftly changing fashion. She never read a news-paper; she only flipped through any magazine that came her way, stopping to look at the horoscope and any photographs of cover girls or well-known people to see what they wore. She claimed, however, that she could learn more easily what she wanted to know merely by keeping an eye open in the street and looking carefully at the dresses displayed in shop windows. She would exclaim: 'That's a clever idea!' Then she would stand a moment, thoughtfully puzzling out the secret of what she had seen. She never took a note. She could memorize anything, however complicated.

Betty bought women's magazines, mostly for the fiction. Sometimes, though she could hardly bear the suspense, she would hold one week's instalment over to the next so that she would have two to read at a time. Edith read nothing at all. She lived her own drama picturesquely, to the full and at a great pace, and she kept the living characters, both the good ones and the bad ones, locked in her head. 'Whereas I,' thought Julia, as her mother continued to examine the sleeves of the dress worn by a platinum blonde mannequin, 'though I am nearly grown up, can still cry copiously over *East Lynne*.' But this she would have confessed to nobody.

The film in the cinema they'd chosen had already begun. Indeed by now it would probably be nearly half over. It seemed a waste of money to pay full price for half a film that did not look very good anyway. Julia's feet throbbed in spite of her low heels, and her stomach was beginning to be repelled by the smell of cooking coming from the restaurants and from stalls selling hot sausages and of the nearness of this slowly moving mass of humanity that didn't apparently know what to do or where to go, but was eternally revolving, whenever she looked up, round the gardens of Leicester Square. She wondered if anybody would ever care if a tidal wave came and swept them all away under the thoughtful eyes of Shakespeare on his pedestal. Was it her aching feet that gave her these depressing thoughts?

On Monday Julia arrived at the store nearly half an hour early. The weekend had brought nothing new or exciting into her life and the sight of her mother starting to dust and to clean the flat had made Julia want to fill her lungs with the air of the streets and to feel the throb of the awakening town in her veins. The store, on her arrival, was only just waking up too. She ran up to the Ladies and inspected herself in the mirror, deciding to change the way she had done her hair. Bending her head down until it was nearly level with her knees she started to brush it vigorously with long, downward strokes, counting each stroke aloud with the firm intention of not stopping till she had reached the fiftieth.

'My goodness!' exclaimed Edith joyfully as she barged into the room. 'That's something I could never do!'

Julia, looking up through a curtain of golden hair, her brush extended in mid-air, looked like a crestfallen child caught in some forbidden act.

'I came early,' she said, trying to laugh.

Edith's expression was transfused with happiness.

'Julia!' she cried. 'You have simply got to meet me at the Italian place for lunch. First to arrive will wait for the other. See? I have had quite the most extra—ordinary weekend!' She paused, breathless. Then: 'Judging by your unhappy face I bet your weekend was a lot less exciting!'

She inspected her make-up in the mirror, pushed back a wisp of dark hair and darted out.

When Julia reached her department Betty had not yet arrived. The dust sheets protecting the sprays and garlands were still in place. Julia removed them, folding the sheets carefully for use in the evening. The little man with his osier trolley came along with a big box of new stock for her department, every spray and headpiece carefully ticketed with the price and number. Monday mornings were generally chosen for rearranging the showcases and displays. There were fewer customers at opening time and those who did make an appearance, exasperated by a too-long weekend with the family, took advantage of their release from cooking, washing-up, family quarrels and jolly but noisy children, to go up into the store's pretty restaurant and order themselves a bun and a quiet cup of coffee. Like a cat slinking out of the house when it is tired of its surroundings, a housewife has several distinct lives.

Julia was delighted, for once, to be alone in the department first thing in the morning. She was proud to be the first to examine the goods sent up by the managerial side. How glad she was to have escaped from home this morning! Before the end of the day she would probably be longing to return to her mother.

When she arrived Betty cast a furious glance at her companion. She hated not to be the first and to see Julia so happily unpacking all that lovely merchandise gave her the impression that her junior was trying to steal her importance and her seniority. Nevertheless, because the slightest quarrel between salesgirls was severely frowned on by the higher grades, Betty put her handbag very silently into the open drawer and gave a hand with the arranging of the flowers.

A moment later Betty's ill-temper had entirely evaporated. She said:

'I am in a frightful temper. The family has been impossible over the weekend. My father received notice from the landlord on Saturday that the rent is to be increased by a third from the first of October next, and what with the rates doubling, he says that it is pretty well the end of the world.' Betty flicked some imaginary dust from the petal of a yellow rose with a very long, pointed, scarlet finger-nail. 'All the family told him he should have bought a house long ago when there were lots of relatively cheap houses in our part of London for sale. He was frightened. He is always frightened and then when he has missed the boat he takes it out of Mother and me. Men are such cowards. He wants me to increase my share of the rent, but how can I? It is up to Father to earn more.'

She turned to Julia in a conciliatory manner.

'What did you do?'

'Nothing.'

'Sundays!' pursued Betty, getting a host of things off her mind. 'Everyone stays in bed reading the papers till midday. Result: The sirloin was only half cooked and the roast potatoes sodden. Mother was furious because I dared to complain and Father just sat there scowling. To think that I could have married that boy and gone with him to Canada!'

Julia looked up in quick surprise. Had she misunderstood or had Betty really uttered those monstrous words? Could it be that Betty had woven in her imagination some mad story concerning Janet's husband—that he had married

155

Janet out of spite because Betty had either refused or ignored him? Might Betty be slipping unconsciously into the category of embittered old maids?

For Julia, keyed up in expectation of her meeting with Edith, the morning passed slowly, but at mid-day she ran out into Regent Street wondering who would be first at the rendezvous. On the way she almost collided with Francis, the young window dresser whose gay smile of recognition reminded her of the mornings that now seemed so long ago when she and Edith sat together addressing envelopes or smoothing out crumpled tissue paper. She almost regretted them as if they were a treasured part of her youth.

Edith had not arrived. As the café had not yet begun to fill up, Julia was able to choose a quiet corner table beside the coffee percolator. Lydia, the girl behind the counter, who had married the young owner, Umberto, shortly after Christmas, was in an advanced stage of pregnancy. Curiously enough, she seemed to be gaining weight all over. Her arms, for instance, were enormous. As for her maternity dress, it looked like a sack bursting at the seams. Did she mind? No! She laughed with pure joy at the whole, wonderful adventure. Her husband and her stepbrother owned several of these cafés and she had worked in the one in Fleet Street, where the romance had started. Her husband came from a village on the Adriatic coast of Italy, while she was a London girl. Julia liked to talk to her. At the time of her marriage she and Julia were equally slim. Looking at her now, Julia thought, laughing: 'That is what seven months' bliss can do to a girl!'

Edith was very late. Nearly twenty minutes out of Julia's time had gone. The young father-to-be was briskly polishing the already bright chrome of the coffee machine. His wife said to Julia: 'I am planning to go on working until the last moment. We are so busy that I want to help my husband all I can. He is such a darling. You have no idea. We are terribly in love.'

Edith arrived with great signs of having hurried. Putting

156

her handbag on the table and looking round to order a coffee and a sandwich she said: 'I simply could not come earlier. I was kept by an unusually difficult customer.'

'One of the bad-tempered kind?' asked Julia.

'On the contrary, rather sweet. She was a customer of Mabel, the girl who left us after that unfortunate incident when a customer claimed to have had her handbag stolen, when she was left for a moment or two in a fitting-room all by herself. This elegant, obviously wealthy, woman wanted to know why Mabel was not there. I told her that Mabel's mother felt that she had been working too hard and insisted that her daughter should have a long rest. "Where is she now?" "I have no idea, Madam." "You know very well where she is. You do not want to give me the name of her firm?" "I do not even know if she is working, Madam." "I had great confidence in her good taste," said the customer. "You are right," I answered. "She was an excellent salesgirl and extremely conscientious. Nevertheless may I try, Madam, to do as well?" "Of course," she said, laughing. "Why not? I want something really elegant but in which I feel perfectly happy. Do you know what I mean? I buy a dress for my own satisfaction. I have learnt not to believe entirely the compliments people pay me any longer. It is the price one pays for growing rich and having an important husband. Let me see if I can learn to rely on your good taste." I brought her the little black model in crêpe georgette which is quite the prettiest thing in the department. She put it on, listened to what I had to say about it and said: "Now show me some others." I showed her nearly twenty dresses and she tried them on, every single one. Remembering that you were here waiting for me, I felt terrible. I said to her: "Would you like me to fetch our buyer, Madam? Perhaps she could help us." "No, no," said my customer. "She would only pay me compliments I don't believe. They are all the same. I have already made my choice. By bringing me immediately that little black dress in crêpe georgette you have given me excellent proof of your capability. You are quite right. It is by far the prettiest dress in the department and I merely wanted to try on the others to confirm my opinion. I hope I have not wasted too much of your time. What is your name? I shall ask for you every time I come." "Thank you, Madam," I said. "It has been a real pleasure." She looked at me and said: "That is why I chose to come on a Monday morning. I felt sure you would not be too busy." Fancy! The astuteness of it! How could she have guessed that we had this rendezvous. At all events I made a wonderful sale. It was a stupendously expensive model.'

Edith sprang up, seized a tomato sandwich from the counter and returning with it exclaimed: 'Have I time to tell you about my weekend?'

'Enough time to relieve me of some of the tension,' said Julia, laughing. 'How much can you tell in ten minutes?'

The café was beginning to fill up.

'You remember the aunt I met on the Channel steamer going over to Ostend? She has just taken a beautiful flat in a luxury block off the Edgware Road, and she has invited me to go round. She promised not to tell my mother anything that passed between us, that everything we talked about would remain confidential. I liked her for saying that. It gave me the opportunity of renewing contact with the members of my family on my own terms, if you understand what I mean. At all events I would not have considered any other conditions.

'Her husband, incidentally, was away. He goes off on long business trips, leaving her alone. She is free and wealthy but, though a lot younger than Mother, is long past her youth.'

'What does she look like?' asked Julia.

'Growing stout, and I would say unhappy from the way she keeps on twisting her rings round. She probably needs the warmth of a big family round her, if indeed a family does bring one warmth. Mine was no good to me. One believes that it must be fun to live alone, to do exactly what one likes, and then, after a while . . . Oh, well, let us not go into that.'

'Who are you talking about? You? Or your aunt?'

'One always ends by talking about oneself. I am going to

be twenty-four on Wednesday. When I look back I have to admit that I have lost the six most important years of my life, from when I was eighteen until now. When my aunt told me that my young sister, who was practically a child when I left home and who used to be so pleased when I gave her the clothes that were too young for me, was about to be married it made me feel terrible. Do you understand now what I mean when I say that I have wasted six years of my life? Still, it was not for this that I asked you to meet me. It was about the young man who asked you for all those posies for his niece. I lied to you. It was not with Betty that I met him.'

'I know that,' said Julia. 'If it had been with Betty she would have recognized him. Why did you have to lie to me?'

'Why does one ever lie?' asked Edith. 'I met him on the way to the dentist. I had told my chief that morning that I had an appointment with the dentist and she took a selfish pleasure in keeping me until the last moment. I tried to find a taxi and decided that if I walked as far as Oxford Street, crossed over and dived behind D. H. Evans I would find one there. It all took much longer than I thought. By the time I had reached Henrietta Place with still no sign of a cab, I was in a panic. An expensive-looking car driven by a young man, with a young woman beside him, drew up at the kerb, and the young man said: "What's the matter? Can we help?" "I have a dentist's appointment," I said, "at the far end of Wimpole Street, and it is already past the time. I just don't know what to do." "Jump in!" said the young man. "We will be glad to take you." I realized that they were brother and sister, and thanks to their kindness I arrived a moment before the secretary came to call me in the waiting-room. When I came out again with half my jaw insensitive from the injection the dentist had given me before filling a tooth, and not even having had time to tidy my hair or make up my face, there in the sunshine was the expensive car waiting for me. Only this time the young man was alone. "Hello," he called out. "I thought you might be feeling pretty terrible after your appointment. One usually does. So can I drive you anywhere? As it happens I have nothing particular to do this morning." "Thanks!" I said, "but I have to get back to work." "It would not prevent us having a quick sherry at the Vintners," he said. "My name is Archie. What's yours?"'

Edith looked up anxiously at the clock.

'That's how we met!' she said.

'I think it's romantic,' said Julia. 'I am glad it happened that way.'

'What I wanted to tell you was this,' said Edith. 'Getting to know this young man who comes from my own part of the country was the reason I went to see my aunt. I felt I needed a background, somebody of my own family. It made me appear less abandoned.'

'I see that,' said Julia.

She was going to be late, but it did not matter. She would explain everything to Betty.

'What worries me,' said Edith, 'is that Archie is so absolutely perfect—good family, serious in his work, the sort of person one knows will make a success of his life. One can generally tell, don't you think? Yet tremendously gay!'

'Why complain?' asked Julia.

'Because . . . Can't you understand?' said Edith. 'The more wonderful it all is, the more it is going to hurt when it leads to nothing. Because it is bound to lead to nothing.'

Julia pondered. Was there any known method for effacing the past?

Edith exclaimed inconsequently:

'I have to pinch myself to be sure I am not dreaming. Seriously, Julia, should I break it up immediately and convince myself that there is nothing else for me but to become a career girl? What I absolutely refuse to do is to start any sort of an affair. I have ruled that right out. Advise me, Julia! What would your mother advise me to do? All my hard, strong, purposeful life has lost its meaning. I no longer even want to spend a weekend in Paris. What would Archie think of a girl who went off to spend a weekend alone in a French hotel? It doesn't make sense any more.'

'I don't suppose anything does make sense any more,' said Julia thoughtfully, 'when a girl is really in love.'

'At all events,' said Edith, 'I want you to promise me something, that you will wait for me at the usual corner tonight.'

'Why specially tonight?' asked Julia. She sensed a mystery.

'Because he has promised to be there.'

One would have expected that in the circumstances Edith would have preferred to be alone, but she was suddenly frightened. The approach of something that she had long secretly dreamt about now seemed fraught with danger. She had seldom felt so devastatingly alone and unconsciously she was making Julia, so much younger than she was, play the role that should in more normal conditions have fallen to her mother. She needed the support of a person in whom she could safely confide. Betty had a mother, however inadequate, so had Daisy and Iris. Julia and her mother made by their close *entente* the proverbial bundle of sticks. They supported each other morally. In this impending crisis Edith virtually, if one excluded the newly redis-covered aunt, had nobody at all. No girl could be expected to face a crisis all by herself. Girls, by their very nature, were ivy needing a wall to support them. Julia, curiously aware of all this, got up, called for her bill and said: 'Very well. If that is what you want, I will be there.'

While closing the heavy drawer in which the two girls kept their handbags Betty had pinched her index finger so brutally that she had cried out in pain. When Julia arrived five minutes later Betty was feeling sorry for herself, and merely said:

'It does hurt!'

'Never mind,' said Julia hopefully. 'The sun is shining. You will feel better after a black coffee and a stroll past the shops.'

'A stroll with whom?' said Betty, suddenly feeling like tears. 'You and Edith are always together, whereas when it is my turn to go out to lunch I am always alone. It is a pity that you and I can never go out at the same time. I do so need to laugh.'

'Edith isn't very receptive to laughter just now,' said Julia. 'She also was half in tears in spite of the fact that her new young man is obviously very much in love with her.'

'I shall not go out at all,' said Betty, looking miserably at her bruised finger. 'I shall go to the Ladies and pin up my hair. Do you think I shall lose my nail?'

Julia looked at the well-manicured finger with the immensely long, pointed nail and, seeing no trace of damage, said:

'No, and at least if you pin up your hair you will be ready to go out tonight. It won't have been a wasted morning.'

'That's what I think,' said Betty, smiling.

An extremely pretty woman had arrived in the department with a beautiful Borzoi that she held on such a tight leash that one had the impression that she was holding its aristocratic neck. The owner and the dog made a superb picture of aristocratic elegance. The woman had stopped in front of some silk squares signed by various famous couturiers. The Borzoi advanced as near as it could to Julia, putting his head gently against her skirt.

'He won't hurt you,' said the woman amiably. 'Stroke him if you feel like it. His name is Tiny. My son, who gave him to me, inflicted this absurd name on him so that the Borzoi should never, in spite of his beauty, feel superior to the donor. My son has just left to spend a month with a family in Germany. It is the first time he has travelled alone and I have been to see him off at the station.'

Her fingers had strayed from the silk squares to the artificial flowers.

'These bouquets of poppies, daisies and cornflowers are very pretty. I will take three of them. This is a beautiful store and though I knew it, of course, by reputation, I have never been in here before. It is so very light and feminine and judging by yourself a veritable hive of lovely young girls. How old are you?'

'Seventeen.'

'A delightful age, full of shy promise. You make me wish I had a daughter as well as a son. If you will allow me to say so, you have quite the prettiest golden hair!'

Long after the customer and her Borzoi had gone, those words echoed in Julia's ears. Somebody had said that she was a lovely young girl with quite the prettiest golden hair. Who had ever told her such a thing before? Somebody else besides her mother would have liked to have her as a daughter. The sky had opened, showing a glimpse of heaven.

As soon as the tissue paper and the dust sheets had been put over the merchandise Julia bade good-night to Betty and hurried to the staff exit at the back of the store. Here, on a large white deal table near the timekeeper's office, were to be found the packages containing whatever the girls had bought for themselves during the early morning hour set aside for such personal shopping.

The staff, as Edith had first pointed out to Julia, was allowed a considerable price reduction so that not only the girls but also the girls' mothers were very sensible of this privilege and were continually giving their daughters lists of things to buy. A black-jacketed shopwalker stood guard over the table. Girls who had bought something that day handed a numbered ticket to this official who quickly looked up the correct parcel. This evening Julia had a very large one waiting for her. The materials in the store were particularly beautiful and Julia's mother, independently of her dressmaker's ticket, found it extremely advantageous to choose whatever she wanted in advance and then ask her daughter to buy it for her the next morning. As there were quite two dozen parcels waiting to be picked up, Julia was obliged to take her turn and when at last she had been handed it, she saw Edith outside making frantic signs at her.

'If I had guessed that you were going to buy half the merchandise in the store,' she laughed, 'I would have thought twice about waiting for you. We must hurry, or Archie will think we've forgotten him.'

When, from a short distance, she sighted him waiting at the wheel of his car, her whole manner changed. She began to laugh and to gesticulate, recounting a whole lot of nonsense to Julia, turning from time to time to wave good-night to a great number of girls from other departments whom she scarcely knew. In the space of a few seconds she had blossomed out into somebody really beautiful. One wondered how this dark girl flowering like a hibiscus could have come from an English family in the Midlands. Perhaps, thought Julia, her ancestors were of an Irish or Mediterranean race. It was this, of course, that added to her piquancy. She had put on her newest dress, bought perhaps like the former one from her buyer, and she had a perfume which though delicious was unknown to Julia. Had it been given to her by the young French beautician who had sung that pretty, old-fashioned waltz? 'I must ask Betty,' thought Julia.

'Hello, Archie. I think you met Julia in the store?'

'I did indeed,' said Archie. 'She wondered how I had guessed her name. What on earth have you got in that box, Julia?'

'Silver brocade for an evening dress,' said Julia.

'Lucky you! Can we give you a lift?'

'Yes,' said Edith on her behalf. 'Jump in, Julia. We will take you as far as Cambridge Circus. Where are we dining tonight, Archie?'

'We are going to Regent's Park,' he said. 'My sister has given me instructions to bring you home to dinner.'

The two girls were squeezed together in the front next to Archie, and at these words as they were speeding towards Piccadilly Circus Julia felt her companion become tense. This was obviously making their relationship a little more official, bringing it nearer the possibility of an engagement, but also nearer inescapable enquiries into Edith's family and the reasons for her temporary alienation from them.

When they turned from Shaftesbury Avenue into Cambridge Circus, Archie asked: 'Where now, Julia?'

'Outside the Palace Theatre would be perfect,' Julia answered. 'Thanks a lot for the lift.'

She jumped out, a little selfconscious because of the parcel, then watched them disappearing swiftly up Charing Cross Road in the direction of Regent's Park. She was both glad and sorry for Edith, wondering how she would emerge from this family ordeal.

Half way down her street Julia was surprised to see her mother talking to Daisy's mother outside Daisy's house, and as she came nearer she noticed that Daisy's mother was mopping tears from her large, watery blue eyes. For some time past the unfortunate woman had been nearly always in tears. She lived in continual fear, not only of her husband but also of what she supposed the neighbours were whispering behind her ample back. She could not make up her mind to leave the street which had been the scene of all her memories and in which her little girls had played as children. She knew all the small shopkeepers and the stall-holders of Seven Dials, the numbers of the buses that passed down Charing Cross Road and Shaftesbury Avenue. But the very streets and houses had become hostile to her and she felt more and more that she had become a figure of suspicion and blame. She also felt so tired, so exhausted, so absolutely worn out. 'Yes, my dear,' she was saying to Julia's mother, loud enough for Julia to overhear. 'I wake up tired, and I go to bed feeling that it would be a relief for me to die. In the morning my nightmares, instead of disappearing, turn into reality so that I can never shake my misery off my poor shoulders.'

'I know, my dear,' said Julia's mother with real compassion in her voice. 'But if you had no husband like me! It's sad to be a widow!'

'No,' said Daisy's mother. 'It can't be worse, and your little girl is such a good little soul. She is so obedient and docile, as daughters should be. Now my Daisy has come back from Paris with some sort of swelling in her legs. I suppose they made her get up too soon.'

She thus appeared to admit what in public she had kept on denying, that there had been a baby, though whether the baby was stillborn or alive nobody knew or dared to ask.

This pitiful, long-suffering mother whose own legs had for twenty years given her hell was at the end of her tether. In spite of all this, upon noticing the presence of Julia, and not only Julia but the large parcel she was holding rather awkwardly under an arm already embarrassed by her handbag, Daisy's mother showed a mixture of interest and jealousy as she exclaimed with pinched lips:

'You get a big reduction at the store, don't you? Quite a lot more, I suppose, than you would with your dressmaker's card. Five per cent more, at least, so that if you charge your customers full price, the difference is well worth having. I used to tell Daisy that she should take greater advantage than she actually did of the privilege. She bought too many of her dresses from those shops in Shaftesbury Avenue. Now, it's too late. She should have gathered rosebuds while she might, as the saying goes. Not that she will ever want to set foot in that place again. Not after what they did to her.'

'Well,' said Julia's mother. 'My daughter and I must be getting back.'

Julia walked silently by her mother's side. She was not pleased with her. The sight of her mother gossiping so openly with a neighbour in the street had struck her as vulgar. It would merely lead to more gossip. When they reached home and Julia noticed that the table was not set for supper and that there was nothing cooking in the kitchen, her silent anger increased. She felt that when she and her mother, for reasons other than those of Daisy's mother, left the street, she would have no regrets. She was perhaps being unconsciously influenced by Edith's romance with Archie, who doubtless would occupy an increasingly important place in his father's firm, who had such excellent manners and whose sister lived in a Nash house off Regent's Park. This was the sort of marriage Julia felt desirable for herself. It would lift her into a different, more agreeable world and provide a solution for her mother's constant fear about the future. Because Julia was going to have to play almost a man's role in offsetting her mother's futile inability to turn her talent into money. Julia's own tastes also were

166

becoming more complicated. They were not limited, as her mother's appeared to be, to owning an oak wardrobe with a fitted mirror. This she would give her in due course. The handling of those artificial flowers at the store, the almost daily meeting with women of obvious importance, like the woman with the Borzoi, made her wish ardently for a garden of her own with real flowers and for the sort of poise that the wealthy customers showed. If Edith were to leave the store in order to get married to Archie, Julia would miss her more than Edith was likely to miss Julia. The fact was that a great deal, if not all, of Julia's re-thinking had come from daily contact with her friend. Even the garden of Julia's dreams had the smooth green lawns and shady trees that Edith had dreamt about during her moments of deep, troubled sleep under drugs. The elder girl had inspired the younger girl. Archie was the sort of man Julia could fall in love with. But Julia's dreams were occasionally even more ambitious, and in her garden there would be not only a lawn and great trees but also a river for swimming in on hot summer afternoons and a rowing boat so that when she had children they could play by the water.

They opened a tin of sardines and tried to hide their momentary dissatisfaction with each other. They went early to bed, but even with the window wide open the night proved stifling and Julia did not sleep well. The noise of the traffic came to her by fits and starts, first the audience leaving the Palace Theatre, then the drunks coming out of the pubs, the fight for the last buses, the roar of the newspaper vans on their way to Euston, to King's Cross, half across London to Paddington, the heavy lorries bringing fruit and vegetables to Covent Garden Market by way of Seven Dials. Cats howled and shrieked in the churchyard of St Giles where the few remaining tombstones spelt out such fragments of London history as those concerning a man, a friend of Ben Jonson, imprisoned for using his pen too freely, and a woodcutter who had saved Charles II's life after the Battle of Worcester by making him chop faggots under an oak. It was nearly dawn when at last Julia fell into the deep sleep of a young, healthy girl tired out by too many problems above the comprehension of her wit. In the morning she did not hear the alarm clock go. Her mother, getting breakfast in the kitchen, knocked on the partition wall. There was no answer. She removed the milk from the gas flame and, thinking she might be ill, stole softly into Julia's room. The young head with the tousled golden hair lay snugly against the pillow. Her mother thought she had seldom looked more tenderly beautiful and she longed to lift her daughter up and take her in her arms, to whisper in her ear: 'Darling Julia, you will never know how much I love you, how much joy you bring into my life!' She would have loved her to be a small child again, perhaps six or seven years old, so that she would need her every moment of the day and run up to her with all her joys and sorrows. But Julia's mother knew there was a time for everything and that breakfast time when her girl was late for work was not the right moment to turn sentimental. She shook her by the shoulder and said: 'Wake up, lazybones. You will be late for work!' Julia leapt up and hurriedly washed. She called to her mother: 'Do you remember how that girl in the film we saw dressed in less time than it takes to say so? I will put on my make-up and comb out my hair in the Ladies when I get to the store. Is coffee ready?'

She swallowed her coffee, nibbled at a piece of bread and butter and arranged her lovely hair under a silk square. She had sold this silk square to herself and now thought the world of it. One morning when she had arrived earlier than usual at her department, the man with the trolley brought her from the Stores a box of new silk scarves from Paris like the ones the woman with the Borzoi had first stopped to examine. Opening the box Julia had gone through them with little gasps of growing admiration. They were quite the loveliest she had ever seen, fabulously expensive but of the purest, heaviest silk. With the twenty-third she fell immediately, hopelessly, delightfully in love. For several days she left it carefully at the bottom of the pile so that nobody, even Betty, should particularly notice it. When she saw that her treasure remained untouched, and was as lovely as on the first day, she bought it from herself at the usual discount and had it sent down, packed and numbered, as was her right and her privilege, to be handed to her against the corresponding stub by the shopwalker in the frock coat. It had become a talisman. She wore it over her hair or round her neck and everybody admired it.

'Are you ready?' asked her mother tenderly. 'Mind the traffic, won't you? Be careful in crossing Cambridge Circus. I get so nervous when you have gone.'

She still did not dare tell her daughter that she had watched her sleeping and so longed to take her in her arms. Instead, she asked:

'You are not still angry about last night?'

'Of course not,' said Julia, laughing. 'How could I be?'

Julia reached the store just in time. The book closed at three minutes past nine. After this a girl was reported to the management. After three times she was sacked. Betty was examining the day's mail orders which came mostly from the provinces, and she had taken advantage of her own early arrival to purloin the most promising, in other words those that would give her the largest share of commission. Normally the two girls went through the letters together and divided them in strict rotation. Julia attached a great deal less importance to this ritual than did her companion. It never seemed worth her while to quarrel about it, but this morning Betty, whose conscience pricked her somewhat, said in order to excuse herself, though in fact it made it sound a great deal worse: 'You are so fortunate, Julia, not to have bus fares like the rest of us. How many girls can walk to work? I don't suppose it takes you ten minutes. Bus fares are ruining me. They are continually being increased.' She made her announcement in such a self-pitying tone that Julia looked up in surprise and said: 'You don't need to worry. After all, you are the head of the department.'

The soft answer turned away any feeling of bitterness, and Betty particularly needed to put her junior in a happy

169

frame of mind on this particular morning because she had been terribly intrigued the previous evening by the sight of Edith and Julia driving away in that luxurious car next to the wealthy young man who had called at the department to buy a posy for his niece. Once again Betty had the bitter feeling that something stupendous had brushed elusively past her. It reminded her of the fact that she had lost a potential husband to Janet.

Bursting with inquisitiveness, she asked the question that was burning her up:

'Did he take you out to dinner?'

'Who?' asked Julia, surprised.

'The young man in the car of course.'

'Good gracious, no!' said Julia. 'He merely dropped me off in Soho.'

'What happened to Edith?'

'I have no idea,' said Julia truthfully. 'I haven't seen her since.'

'It all seems very strange,' said Betty, discomfited.

Her ill humour dragged on most of the day. When she took her handbag out of the drawer she discovered that she had lost a glove. Curiously enough, she was infuriated by the realization that the person who found it would not even profit from her misfortune. The loss was therefore twofold. She said: 'It's because of the rain. I can never put an umbrella up without losing something.' Julia, who because she was short-sighted never lost anything, so careful were her movements, laughed. She thought it funny. Not un-naturally Betty glanced with angry suspicion at her junior, but, realizing that Julia's laughter was entirely devoid of malice, started to join in it. 'Perhaps you dropped it in the Ladies or while you were putting your umbrella in the locker,' said Julia helpfully. 'Why don't you go and look?'

Betty came back a few moments later holding her lost glove in the air like a trophy. 'I found it suspended above a wash basin,' she said. 'Of course it was not worth stealing. One odd glove.'

'Even two gloves,' said Julia. 'Who would want to steal

gloves? There would be something indecent about wearing another girl's gloves. Gloves are so intimate. Another girl's beret, another girl's shoes, why, yes! One is always doing that. Mother breaks in all my shoes because she takes one quarter size less than I do so that my shoes, even when they are new, don't hurt her. Quite apart from that I have often bought shoes from other girls. But not gloves!'

Betty looked at her in open surprise.

'Sometimes,' she said slowly, 'I think you are a little mad!'

By closing time rain was falling quite heavily. In fact it had been raining on and off all day. Customers had arrived at the store with dripping umbrellas. Julia was wearing light shoes with high heels and before long her feet were wet.

Edith was waiting for her.

'Let's go to Umberto's for a coffee,' she said.

'No,' answered Julia. 'I was late getting up this morning and if I keep Mother waiting now she will either imagine that I'm ill or that I have got the sack. Besides, I would like to change my shoes. I shall ruin these and they are new.'

Regent Street was a mass of damp, struggling humanity trying to board passing buses nearly all of which, being full, did not stop. The conductors gave defiant rings to tell their drivers to pass on. Enmity ran like an electric current between them and the exasperated people in the queues, the spikes of their umbrellas catching against one another. Girls resigned themselves to long, wet, uncomfortable journeys home by bus or tube. Passing cars, their owners safe and dry inside, splashed the girls' stockings and the hems of their skirts. It was miserable.

'I did no shopping,' complained Edith, 'and there won't be a thing worth eating in the flat. None of the girls has enough cash to budget ahead. Why on earth do the shops have to close so early?'

'Whose shops?' laughed Julia. 'Other people's? Or our own?'

Suddenly she exclaimed:

'They would still be open in Soho! Better still, you could come and have supper with us. Mother would be delighted.'

'Thanks, but we can't walk,' objected Edith. 'Not in this rain.'

'You won't get any less wet waiting in a queue for a bus,' said Julia. 'The air will do us good.'

'Very well,' agreed Edith, turning up the collar of her raincoat and drawing close to Julia so that their two bright red umbrellas made a roof over their heads. 'Let's go!'

As they hurried off arm in arm in the direction of Soho Square, Julia asked excitedly: 'Tell me about last night!' At least, she thought, in the anonymity of the narrow streets there would be no indelicate ears to listen to what they said.

'Well,' said Edith, preparing herself, as she fell into step with Julia, to tell the whole story, 'as you know he took me to his sister's house in Regent's Park. She was there waiting for us in the drawing-room having drinks with a man who was to take her to the theatre after dinner. The house is really beautiful, with cream walls hung with valuable pictures, and elegant furniture. Dinner was served at a big round table with little mats of hunting scenes and a bowl of red roses in the centre—the main course was lamb cutlets with paper frills on the bone ranged round mashed potatoes in a silver dish, and afterwards strawberries and cream. They have a Norwegian maid, a real Viking's daughter, no, actually the daughter of an Oslo shipbuilder. Rather sweet and only seventeen. She's supposed to be perfecting her English which she already speaks as well as you and I, except for the tiniest, fascinating Nordic accent, but apparently she could not resist coming for a glimpse of London between college terms. She talked to us all during dinner, as if she were a guest instead of the maid. I was the one to be shy! She was as sure of herself as I have ever seen any girl. She said, as she passed the strawberries round: 'I am in a hurry tonight. I am going dancing with a boy-friend at the Norwegian club. I must not keep him waiting."
"That's all right," said Archie's sister. "Just stack everything in the kitchen. Archie and our friend Edith will keep an eye on the children." She gave me the sweetest smile.

"You don't mind me calling you Edith?" "Oh, no!" I cried. The two children, both girls, the elder is ten, were already in bed, Archie's sister explained. Though not asleep of course. One was engrossed in *Little Women*. The other was looking at a book of fairy tales. Archie's sister added: "I will go up and get my fur coat." She rose quietly and superbly. The whole house had an air of extraordinary happiness, of confident affection, as if nobody could ever quarrel in it, as if there were no such vexations as ill humour or quarterly bills. Archie went to make coffee in the kitchen, asking me to go and help him. His sister and her escort stood in the hall, waiting to go, she wearing her fur coat, smelling of French perfume. "Goodbye, Archie," he called. "I'll see you at the club tomorrow." The Norwegian girl disappeared in a delighted flurry and the big house fell suddenly silent.

'We were supposed, as I say, to keep an eye on the two girls. I said to myself as Archie poured out brandy in balloon glasses: "This is the carefully prepared moment. This is the trap, the snare, into which I am supposed to fall—the rich man and the shop-girl in a fine house from which everybody, except two little girls upstairs, has flown." There were sofas, divans, soft lights and music from a gramophone, just everything to seduce a girl. The girl, believe me, was full of rancour. She was determined not to be trapped a second time. Even the coffee in her mouth had a bitter taste and brandy in balloon glasses is a classical addition to the final scene. As I don't smoke there was no way of calming my nerves except by biting on my lips or clenching my hands. But at the same time, Julia darling, I did not want to play the role of an idiot girl. I wanted to come out of it with flying colours, as the saying goes. But I felt awful. You remember the dress I was wearing, sleeveless and so short, and underneath I was practically naked. He put down his brandy glass and said: "I had better go up and see how the girls are. They are such little devils. At one minute they are safely tucked up in bed; at the next they are down in the kitchen raiding the larder." He laughed and

173

was gone, running swiftly up the stairs. "That's it!" I told myself. "He wants to make certain we are not going to be disturbed." He was soon back looking radiant. "One of them is still reading," he announced, "the other is crying. She says that Red Riding Hood is being attacked by the wolf. I don't pretend to understand them. Girls are such enigmas. Would you like to come up and see them? Would it amuse you?" I cried: "I would just love to!" "That's the girl!" he said. "They will both fall in love with that beautiful dress you are wearing."

'They were in quite the daintiest room with such a thick carpet that my high heels sank into the pile. Each had her own little bed, and on the dressing-table, which had animals painted on either side of the cheval mirror, was the diadem of gardenias that Archie had bought, amongst other things, from you. He took it up to show me and said: "When the girl you share your flat with told me that you were having dinner with a colleague from the store and her mother, I just could not feel sure she wasn't lying. I thought you were out with another man. So I used this excuse to check up. I could have put my arms round your friend Julia when I discovered you had not brushed me off with a lie. I could not go on loving a girl who had tried to trick me. I hate girls who lie!"'

They had arrived almost without knowing it, at the far side of Soho Square. As the rain, that had been abating, was suddenly whipped up again by a passing squall, which beat against the trees in the gardens and sent people running for shelter, the two girls lowered their umbrellas and passed into the Catholic church of St Patrick where evening Mass was being sung. The church was so full that the congregation overflowed into the entrance where there was a chapel with lighted candles and some copies of the church magazine. The two girls picked their way through the kneeling crowd into the back of the church where they knelt to say their individual prayers.

When, at last, they reached Julia's place her mother was not there. The girls felt suddenly quite lost. The bright lights of Soho and the vividness of Edith's tale had both faded away. 'Take your raincoat and shoes off,' said Julia, trying to play the role of hostess. 'I will lend you some slippers. Mother is sure to be back soon.' But in spite of everything that Julia could do, the flat was inhospitable without the warm presence of her mother. The kitchen had neither warmth nor food. The furniture in the living-room appeared shoddy. 'Oh, what can have happened to mother?' cried Julia after a while. She was beginning to feel anxious about her mother's safety and increasingly ashamed of what Edith would be secretly thinking. Edith was, in fact, showing signs of impatience. Julia wished she could find something that would interest her friend, to take her mind off the boredom of waiting and to impress her. This *contretemps* might even have the effect, she thought, of alienating her friend's affection for ever. She did so need her guidance and friendship.

After a quarter of an hour's mutual agony, light steps were heard on the stairs and Iris burst into the room. 'Your mother says that you are not to worry,' she said breathlessly to Julia. 'My mother has been taken ill and your mother is sitting with her till the doctor comes. Daisy has not come home yet.'

'Isn't your father there either?' asked Julia. She was much more anxious than she appeared to be, but her natural expansiveness was reduced by the presence of Edith. Fear of Edith's criticism chilled her.

'Father is at work,' said Iris. 'He is unloading fruit in Covent Garden Market.'

'How terrible!' exclaimed Julia, suddenly filled with compassion. She no longer minded if her disarray were visible or not. How she longed to be with her mother.

Iris collapsed on a chair. In her distraction she had lost the bright quality of her youth and looked as if she were already carrying the responsibilities of a family on her narrow shoulders. When she spoke of her father one had the strange impression that she was talking of a difficult husband. She said: 'I have made him up a bed in another room. Mother must not be disturbed. I shall spend the night in a chair at the foot of her bed in case she needs anything.' What a frail edifice it all sounded! The mother ill, Daisy, at least for the moment, a broken reed, the ineffectual father, the girl in her teens trying to manage. Could she hold it together or would it fall apart? But Iris had already risen to the occasion as women invariably do, whatever their age. 'I have made him up a bed . . .' she had declared. 'I shall spend the night in a chair . . . in case she needs anything.'

'I must run!' she said, getting up, re-charging her slender form with energy. 'Maybe the doctor has already arrived!'

She ran to the window, looked out, but saw nothing.

'When Daisy comes home, I shall tell her what I think of her! She has done enough harm to mother and to me!' Her tone had become violent, possessive. She went on, addressing her anger to the empty street: 'If from the beginning there had been just Mother and me, none of this would have happened. Everything would have been all right.' She turned round and faced Julia. 'As it is with you and your mother,' she said. 'Nobody to stand in your way!'

Julia, looking at her, thought: 'She is not the same girl as the one I went dancing with only the other night. Can a girl grow into a woman overnight? Shall I change so quickly, so devastatingly?'

Iris ran out of the room and down the stairs, and in the silence that followed Julia and Edith again felt embarrassed. Julia was ashamed that her friend had been there to witness this scene. Edith felt that in the circumstances it would not be proper for her to take up, where she had left off, the account of her adventures in the house in Regent's Park. Temporarily the link between them had snapped. Julia picked up the evening paper and looked absent-mindedly at a photograph on the back page, then she threw it down saying: 'It's sport!' Edith laughed. The two girls could not understand in their little feminine hearts that in a world so full of human suffering, men could be so childish as to amuse themselves with a bat and a ball. Julia had put the kettle on and it was now filling the small kitchen with steam, but she reflected that any sort of meal was unthinkable while her mother was absent. It would somehow be disloyal. Edith felt a longing to be back in her own flat where she could change her dress and do some ironing. One of the other girls might be home and they could gossip over supper. She had been a fool to come here with Julia in the rain.

'Julia darling,' she exclaimed, getting up. 'Forgive me. I am doing no good here. I'll see you at the store tomorrow.'

Julia nodded. She said in a flat, disillusioned voice:

'At least the rain has stopped.'

At nine o'clock Julia's mother came home.

'The doctor says it's pneumonia,' she declared, going into the kitchen and filling the whole flat with her presence. 'There are drugs, of course, but the doctor says she is worn out. Her heart may not stand it.'

'You mean it could be serious?' asked Julia.

'Very serious,' said her mother.

'Did Daisy come home? I kept on looking out of the window but I saw nobody. I think I fell asleep.'

'Yes, Daisy came home,' Julia's mother said, 'but all she did was to sit in a chair and smoke one cigarette after the other. She behaved as if she were a stranger to what was taking place. She has a new job, a very good one, I gather, and enough money to start buying herself a new dress at one of those dress shops in Shaftesbury Avenue. She had the audacity to show it to me.'

'I suppose Old Madam is still about?' asked Julia, laying the table. Everything was returning to normal. Eggs were frying. Coffee was filling the flat with a delicious, warm, homely smell.

'Old Madam?' Julia's mother repeated, bringing the coffee and the eggs to the table, and settling down opposite her daughter. 'I am not very concerned with that old dear, except that she probably lent money to Daisy and is anxious to get it back. I fear both of them are getting a little involved in their own fairy tales. Daisy is said to have told a neighbour who was unwise enough to question her, that she had never been pregnant and that there was accordingly no baby, either here or in Paris. She also said that her new employer had advised her to report any suggestion of slander of this kind to her solicitor. That, perhaps, is the best solution. Personally, I'm merely concerned with her mother. When Iris came over in a panic to fetch me, I found her mother gripping the kitchen table, unable to move. We undressed her and put her to bed. She had just finished the week's wash and was obsessed by the fact that it had been a particularly heavy one and that she hadn't been able to hang it up on a line in the yard. I fancy that whatever worries she may have had about Daisy were magnified by the fact that she is just starting her menopause. I promised Iris I would go round in the morning and help her with the wash. The trouble about us women is that we make mountains out of relatively small things such as hanging up the sheets and pillow cases on the line. Until I can put her mind at rest on this matter she will go on tormenting herself and make her doctor's task more difficult. Little Iris has been a brick all along. She has turned herself into a real little woman.'

'That is precisely what I thought,' said Julia.

Her mother shot a quick glance at her. She felt proud of her daughter's perspicacity. They were both at ease now and the evening ended much more happily than it had begun. Julia decided to change the position of the couch. 'It would look better near the window,' she said. Her mother was careful not to oppose this desire, having noticed that her daughter's bouts of furniture moving inevitably coincided with certain days in the month. Thus she would find herself reassured on a matter concerning her daughter's good conduct about which she would never have dared to question her.

She was perhaps more than ordinarily relieved this evening to note that all was well on this score. An attractive girl was surrounded by perils that simply had not existed when she was young—yes, a girl had to have her head screwed on tight these days, as she was pretty certain, or at least as she very much hoped, Julia had hers. There was also another danger which Julia's mother hardly liked to think about. She had a feeling, perhaps it was only a feeling, that her clientele was slowly diminishing. The mere material of a dress, quite apart from its making up, cost more than a good ready-to-wear. There remained the exceptional customer who was not so well proportioned, the woman who had a narrow waist and wide hips, and the woman who had a sort of cult for carefully finished seams or hand-made buttonholes. The fact remained, however, that if the clientele dwindled beyond a certain point there would be no question of moving to a better flat, which would greatly please Julia. Even this one might prove to be too expensive in time. What a multitude of nightmares it would be if, as alas *could* happen, she or Julia were to fall ill or if something happened to disrupt the rhythm of their modest existence.

She said to her daughter:

'I am beginning to think there is no future for my sort of home dressmaking. I simply can't compete.'

'Edith thinks you are wonderful!' said Julia.

'Perhaps, but I am miserably paid,' said her mother. Then more bravely: 'Oh, well, I suppose lots of people are less fortunate than we are!'

'Lots are a great deal richer!' exclaimed Julia with a touch of bitterness. 'I have been at the store for nearly a year and where have I got to? Time counts if something is to come my way!'

On Monday morning Mrs Davies came back from her holiday in Spain. The strong Mediterranean sun had given her a deep, becoming tan, but, to her dismay, the unaccustomed food and an orgy of excellent fish fried in olive oil had made her put on a little weight, a fact brought vividly home to her by the way that the petersham in the waistband of her black skirt pinched her. Her husband had attained high speeds with his new car on the French roads, and he had done some sailing. Though Mrs Davies was physically back at work she was not yet mentally adjusted to her store routine. Not that she particularly regretted her holiday or in any way desired an idle life. What was beginning to worry her, and to make her dissatisfied, was a lack of *raison d'être*, an aim, a valid goal. Being childless, the money she earned at the store, an excellent salary for a woman, was in the main put to such uninspiring uses—to help her husband buy a new and faster car every year, and quite unnecessary things for the house. There comes a time in every woman's life when she looks back in an effort to assess her achievements, but in her case she had been unable even to have a child, which at least would have been an act of creation.

People were, of course, very polite to her in the store. There she was definitely somebody. The moment she walked out of it, by comparison with any successful actress, a film star, or even one of the dwindling aristocracy, she was just nobody. This thought riled her.

She was in no particular hurry to go down to her department. She had brought one or two small presents for the girls, but she was in no mood just now to listen to their tales and complaints. They were nice enough in their way, especially the little one with her polite manner and golden hair (to whom she must try not to show favouritism), but they would soon leave without a goodbye or a thank you, and be replaced by two other girls whom she would be obliged to train and to flatter.

She decided to call on her colleague, the buyer of the dress department, but she was not to be found. A girl adjusting a dress on a mannequin was humming a tune from an American musical.

It was Edith with her mouth full of pins, trying to give the right curves and pinches to the little black dress. The breasts must look round and sexy, the waist tiny, the hips smooth and almost polished. Gazing at the girl so busy at her work Mrs Davies felt jealous of her exotic beauty and her sparkling youth, just as Edith, when she suddenly looked up and saw the elegant buyer of her friend's department, felt jealous of her poise and importance.

Edith was not at all put out at being discovered arranging her little black number. She was not shy. This was perhaps her strongest point. She said:

'Do you like it? It's very young, don't you think? The sort of dress you can get into and out of in a split second!'

She laughed and her gaiety was infectious.

'You are quite right,' said Mrs Davies, falling quickly into the routine of her profession. 'You have given me an idea about some rather effective Japanese painted wood necklaces in brilliant pink and brown. Where is your buyer?'

'She is in Manchester,' said Edith. 'I don't expect her back till tomorrow.'

Edith stood back like a painter to admire her handiwork. 'I'm trying to get everything straight before the crowds arrive,' she said. 'This dress and one or two others feature in the national press this morning. You have probably seen the papers. I won't even try to get out to lunch. That should prove by far our busiest time.'

'I see that you are very enthusiastic,' said Mrs Davies.

'Passionately,' said Edith, laughing, and without the slightest desire to impress. 'As soon as I get out into Regent Street I start looking at what the other stores feature in their windows. Sometimes I go up to their dress departments, partly because I love to handle dresses and partly as a self-appointed, unofficial spy! It amuses me to hear some young salesgirl ask me: "What can I do for you, Miss?" When she asks that I give her my sweetest smile and answer: "Do you mind if I just look around?" And of course she always says: "Certainly, Miss."'

Mrs Davies returned thoughtfully to her office and went quickly through the morning papers that had remained untouched on her desk, another lapse due to the left-over holiday spirit. In one or two of them she saw reproductions of the little black dress, but the salesgirl called Edith who was a friend of Julia's, if she were not mistaken, had made it more glamorous than it looked in the papers. She must have magic fingers. The mannequin's absurd blonde wig had helped, of course, to set off the dress. The hair style was so *bouffant* that it made the shoulders look slimmer. She went to the restaurant where the little round tables with their rose damask cloths gave the effect of a parterre of flowers. The waitresses all stopped talking when she arrived, bade her good-morning and enquired if she had enjoyed her holiday. Had it been very hot in Spain? She asked for a cup of black coffee, but when it came, though she did not dare say anything, she found it neither hot enough nor strong enough.

Going down into the department she found Betty with a harrowed face, telling Julia about a road accident in which a girl of their own age had been hit by a bus and terribly mutilated. The white-haired man delivering the provincial mail stood by his basket, listening to Betty. He found her touching and exuberant with youth, and he told himself that when the time came for him to retire and live with his son's family in Mitcham, what he would miss most would be the inconsequent talk of these young girls who, as in the Bible, warmed his drying bones. Every other day, it seemed to him, they changed the style of their hair, the tone of their make-up and nail varnish. What a lot of delightful things there were for a girl to do! When he was young he had thought girls nice but stupid. Now he considered them like flowers in a herbaceous border, very pleasing to the eye. Mrs Davies was about to break in on this entirely irregular scene when a young woman came briskly into the department carrying a purchase in a cardboard box. Advancing towards Julia, she said: 'I wonder if you would help me? I have just bought the prettiest little black dress, like the one advertised in the morning paper, and as I wanted something to brighten it up, the salesgirl advised me to get one or two gardenias. She said I was to ask for Miss Julia. Are you Miss Julia?'

'Yes, I am,' said Julia.

'I thought so. She said I had to look out for a very young girl with golden hair.'

Mrs Davies, stepping lightly back out of sight, smiled. So

Edith had made her first sale and was extending her success to another department. What a girl! If Mrs Davies knew anything about the business she would predict that it would not be long before Edith became a store buyer. This incident had given her a desire to get back to work. She had even forgotten to tell the two girls that she had received a card from Janet in Toronto, saying that she was extremely happy and hoped to come to London with her husband for their vacation next summer.

5

'HE doctor,' said Iris importantly, 'thinks she is getting along as well as can be expected.'

On her way home Julia had stopped to ask her friend who stood just inside her front door for news about her mother. Now that Iris had put her mind at rest on this point, Julia said: 'What on earth are you doing half in and half out of your door like this?'

'I have ten shillings on the three-thirty,' said Iris. 'I'm waiting for the paper boy. After I've looked at the racing results my father will take the paper to bed with him. Now that he has to sleep alone, he likes something to read.'

Iris assumed her grown woman look.

'I took a day off from the office,' she said, 'so that your mother and I could finish the entire wash—everything that my mother had already begun, and all the rest that had still to be done. Mountains of wash, and now it is all hanging up in the yard. Do you think it's going to rain?'

'I hope not,' Julia answered, scanning what was visible of the sky in the direction of the Palace Theatre.

Iris had pulled her hair away from her forehead and tied it back with the ribbon from an old chocolate box. This in itself gave her quite a different air, but what perhaps was most remarkable about her appearance was that she was wearing one of her mother's starched aprons far too big for her, so that she looked overdressed in front and under-dressed behind. In normal circumstances, Julia would have howled with laughter, but she remembered that somewhere behind the narrow corridor her friend's mother was lying extremely ill.

On reaching home, Julia found her mother wearing her

good deed of the day expression. Her mother certainly felt that the whole street must know about her role in the mountainous wash that she and Iris had got through between ten o'clock in the morning and six at night.

'You just can't imagine,' Julia's mother told her, laying the table for supper. 'All those sheets that had lain in various odd corners collecting dust and grime and that needed boiling. She had the same sort of passion for sheets as little boys have for postage stamps, inheriting them, picking them up at sales, borrowing them and stealing from the housekeeping money to buy new ones. She was afraid of her husband (small wonder when one hears his booming voice), and even of Daisy. Speaking of Daisy, we ran into real trouble. While Iris and I were emptying out an old cupboard we found a small pile of £5 notes that her mother had hidden between some sheets. Presumably she had hidden them from "him". Most women have a thing about hiding money. I have done it myself and I wouldn't be surprised if when you have a home of your own you do the same. Men never understand that a woman wants cash.

'When Daisy saw the money she flew into a rage. Here she had been obliged to borrow from Old Madam at an exorbitant rate of interest, money not yet fully repaid. So how could her mother have forced her to submit to such an indignity when she had all those good £5 notes hidden away doing nobody any good? This was, of course, the first time that Daisy had ever admitted borrowing money for anything from anybody. At any rate, she was so furious that while Iris and I were hanging up the washing in the yard, she began throwing her clothes into a suitcase and swearing loud enough for all the neighbours to hear that she would go to the Channel Islands and never set foot in her parents' house again.'

'Do you think she really will?' asked Julia.

'I think she already has,' said her mother. 'I am not at all sure that it was not all arranged before the scene of the £5 notes. She spoke about having the offer of a job in an hotel where she would be fed and lodged. I think it might be quite a good idea for her. She would do it very well, and she might even find a husband.'

After a moment's reflection Julia's mother added:

'You know, Daisy is basically a good girl and a splendid worker. Youth can make mistakes and that is hardly surprising when I consider that I still make as many as I did when I was a young girl. But Daisy has her typing and shorthand and when a girl knows how to do something supremely well, she should always have a better chance than another girl to recover her balance. My own feeling is that Daisy is showing as much determination now as she showed little during her pregnancy.'

'But if she has had a baby, what has happened to it?'

Julia's mother was not inclined to discuss this question except to say that she had heard somewhere that there were seldom enough babies available for adoption, so presumably there would have been no difficulty for Daisy, if she had desired to do so, to dispose of the child. 'She may have decided from the start that she wanted to have the baby but was unwilling to keep it. No two girls in an emergency react in the same way.'

As Julia went to work the next morning she remembered that Edith had never finished her account of what happened in the house in Regent's Park. The two girls found it increasingly difficult to get enough time together. They would invariably promise to meet during the lunch hour, but the exact timing was, for a number of reasons, difficult. One could hardly expect Edith, for instance, while attending to a difficult customer, suddenly to announce that she had a girl-friend waiting for her at the corner of the street! It was much to Julia's credit that they never quarrelled even when Edith ruined her lunch hour. But Julia had been taught infinite patience by her mother. Though in some respects highly volatile, passing from one extreme of emotion to another, she had been taught to remain quietly in what her mother called a proper, ladylike position, her back straight, her legs tightly together, her hands always busy. Except, of course, if she were reading; but that depended on the time and the book. Reading was not so useful as sewing or knitting. Be that as it may, while Julia waited for Edith the next day, an Edith who might or might not turn up, she sat with her back to the lockers in the Ladies Room and tried to concentrate on *Shirley*. She was unable to concentrate fully because she was planning between each line to knit herself before the weekend a close-fitting jersey with bright stripes and a tiny neck that would adequately stress her well-proportioned femininity. She would wear this with a short, pleated skirt. She thought of it as the ideal ensemble for going out dancing in the rain! And between lines of Charlotte Brontë and her plans about the pullover, she would bite into a sandwich her mother had provided for her before she had left home.

At this moment, Edith burst into the room and exclaimed:

'What a silly place to wait for me! I went out to look for you in the street.'

Then, glancing at the small package beside Julia, she said: 'Are these Cheddar?'

'Yes,' said Julia. 'Just Cheddar.'

'I like Cheddar better than any cheese,' said Edith, starting to devour one. 'You can have all the foreign varieties for one piece of lovely fresh Cheddar.'

'I agree,' said Julia.

The two girls were now seated next to each other, munching Cheddar sandwiches. Edith's eyes, beady and alert, were like those of a bird examining the country beyond its perch. Indeed they quickly picked out something of interest.

'Those three girls washing their hands,' she said suddenly. 'They are new, aren't they?' Julia looked at them intently, but because she was short-sighted they merely made a rather picturesque blur. 'I expect they are,' she said. 'So what?'

'Don't you rather wonder to what department they are being assigned?' asked Edith. 'It doesn't concern us,' said Julia. 'Anybody would think that you were responsible for the running of the whole store.' Edith looked at her with affectionate pity. 'As long as I work here,' she said patiently, 'that is more or less how I do feel.'

Julia jumped up, brushed the crumbs from her skirt, gathered up her book and her handbag and said:

'Keep the rest of the sandwiches. I must run!'

On the staircase she bumped into Francis. She blushed scarlet.

'Excuse me,' said Francis.

'Oh, I'm sorry!' said Julia.

They laughed.

'You have become very pretty,' said Francis as if something were wrong.

'You think so?'

'It would be nice to see you in some other place than on these stairs. One evening, for instance, for something to eat. Might I take you to some amusing café in the Brompton Road? Or, of course, any other place you preferred?'

'I would have to ask Mother,' said Julia.

'I did not know that girls still asked their mothers. You must be unique!'

'I think I probably am,' said Julia. 'But if the idea puts you off?'

'Good heavens' no!' he said. 'Just the opposite. The more difficult you make it sound, the more I feel that I want to get to know you. You wouldn't need to be chaperoned, would you?'

Julia laughed.

'No, not as bad as that. Incidentally, I imagined that you must have left. I haven't seen you around.'

'I have been to America, as a guest of a store in Chicago. Then to Seattle and home by way of New York. I am due for a lot of sleep. I only arrived home last night. Suppose we were to meet on Friday evening? Would that suit you?'

'That will suit me,' said Julia mischievously, wondering all the same if it were true.

'Well,' she thought, as she walked slowly back to her department. 'Does this mean that he no longer sees the girl from the General Office?' What had happened to her?

Once upon a time she had appeared so sure of herself, so sophisticated. She might have left the store, for all Julia knew. Other thoughts passed through her mind. This invitation from Francis, doubtless unimportant in itself, would at least prove to Edith, who was always laughing at her, though in a kindly way, that she, Julia, was capable of having dates. She hoped that Edith would take due note. As for Julia's mother, she might, of course, on first being told the news, try to curb, out of natural prudence, her enthusiasm, but she could scarcely help being pleased, even a little proud, that her daughter was invited out by a young man who had just come back from a business trip across the North American continent. There were times when her mother seemed almost to resent Julia's exaggerated dutifulness in returning every evening to her mother's side. Though it was appallingly unfair, the fact remained that virtue in a girl was sometimes unappreciated by those for whom she sacrificed herself. Quite a number of girls went so far as to remain single until late in life in order to look after their widowed mothers, and this possibility had given Julia a kind of heartburn when she thought about it. A middle course was always difficult to tread. It was to be hoped that once she had begun to go out with a man (that is what was so exciting about it) she would not be tempted to throw her bonnet over the windmill. Still, she reflected, she was only seventeen—eighteen before the end of the month.

Only a few minutes after Betty had gone to lunch, Julia looked up to see Mrs Davies standing on the fringe of the department in the attitude of a customer. This impression was strengthened by the fact that she was holding her beautiful crocodile handbag, the one with the real gold clasp. 'What is she doing here at this hour?' thought Julia nervously. 'There must have been a complaint or else a customer has sent back her purchase with an angry note.'

For once Julia was thoroughly frightened. At her age the fear of getting the sack is either non-existent or else, as in her case, immense. She told herself during these next few minutes of fear that she had probably begun to take her life in the store too much for granted. After nearly a year she thought of herself as part of the organization, almost as indispensable, and no doubt took risks and was too much carried away by Edith's confidence and sure-footedness. She reflected that only last night her mother had become suddenly afraid that her dressmaking might slowly disappear as a source of income.

Julia opened the drawer where she and Betty kept their things and took out a small sample of a French eau de Cologne that one of the girls in Perfumery had given her a few days earlier. Snapping off the top, she allowed the cool, scented alcohol to pour over her wrists. She must not panic or she would begin to sweat. That was one of the curses of being young.

Several customers had appeared from nowhere and she began hastily to serve them. They gave her no difficulty and she made a number of rapid sales. When she looked again in the direction of Mrs Davies she saw that she had moved over to the handbag and stocking department and was talking to its buyer. When Betty came back from lunch Julia, quite recovered, longed to ask her what in her opinion Mrs Davies had been doing on a tour of inspection at that unusual hour. On second thoughts, she decided to say nothing. Why should she make Betty a gift of her moment of fear?

Arriving home early Julia had a pleasant surprise. Her mother, who had found herself with unexpected free time, had cut an autumn coat for her daughter. The material was a splendid red worsted which she had bought some weeks earlier at the store; the lining would be put together from various lengths cunningly saved from customers' orders. Thus the coat would work out very reasonably and it would look gay and autumnal when worn over the proverbial 'little black dress'. Julia laughed with delight. Yet she knew that as soon as her mother began to make something special for her, she would receive an unexpected flood of orders, and the result would be that the 'something special' for her daughter would remain untouched for the next few weeks at the side of her work table. Nevertheless mother and daughter went carefully into the design. The bodice was to be close fitting and the skirt flared. Tomorrow Julia would go to an Oxford Street shop during her lunch hour to see if she could find outstandingly pretty buttons.

There were times, of course, when Julia would have preferred, like many other girls, like Daisy, for instance, to have gone to those fascinating shops in Oxford Street or New Bond Street, and bought a coat or a dress ready to wear. But what was a girl to do when she had been brought up by a widowed dressmaker who had instilled into her a sort of taboo? Edith had shown the tact of a veritable ambassadress that evening when she had come to Julia's home and admired the dress her mother was making. Of course the dress was beautiful. Everything made by an expert by hand is better (if better is the word) than what is run up in huge quantities on machines. But Edith did not need to be told that the dresses she herself sold so cleverly all day had a charm which, for many modern girls, made the quick, easy purchase of ready-made much more fun than the elaborate complications that attended hand-made clothes. One day when Julia was free, when she was married, for instance, she would break the taboo and indulge in an absolute orgy of cheap, effective, colourful ready-to-wear! Unless, of course, the taboo was already too deeply ingrained in her.

Julia did not meet Edith again until the following evening. Both Betty and she were in a hurry to leave the store and they started to cover everything up as soon as the closing bell rang. The two girls had learnt to throw the covers over the various stands with accuracy and grace, and they often found themselves deploring the fact that so much skill had been acquired for something that would prove so utterly useless in the future.

Julia had no sooner emerged into Regent Street than Edith sprang on her from behind. She let out a cry of fear, whereupon both of them broke into the happiest peals of youthful, silvery laughter.

'I must talk!' said Edith.

'Where?' asked Julia.

'The foyer of the Plaza,' said Edith. 'There are gorgeous carpets and seats and we can pretend we are waiting for a gentleman-friend.'

They entered brazenly and sat on the edge of a sofa, very erect and uncomfortable because of the usher in uniform who looked at them with what they feared was suspicion. Edith said:

'Keep looking up anxiously for the arrival of our presumed escort. We must not let them think that we are a couple of tarts soliciting.'

Julia's laughter rose up again.

'Do you think we look like tarts?' she asked.

She had come out of the Ladies in such a hurry that she had not given her make-up the usual careful attention. The silly side of this was that during her lunch hour, when she went to choose the buttons for her red coat, she had bought some light blue eye-shadow, and she was now vexed not to have made use of it before coming out.

'I love Thursday nights,' said Edith. 'Just look at these crowds.'

After a moment Edith said:

'If this sofa were mine, I could sit right back in it and relax. The same goes for the carpet, I would enjoy walking over it more if it happened to be in my own home.'

'I wonder if Mother and I will have a home much longer to put a carpet in,' said Julia. 'Yesterday I thought I was going to get the sack, and as Mother seemed convinced that she is on the point of losing her last customers, things are pretty black. I wish I were as sure of myself as you are!'

Edith turned and faced her squarely.

'I never cease being afraid,' she whispered. 'If my buyer feels that I am really a danger to her, she will sack me right away. It would be a pity, but she would not hesitate.'

'I wish I could talk to others as I talk to you,' said Julia. 'Tomorrow night I shall be tongue-tied because I have a date with Francis.'

192

'Francis?' Edith queried.

'The young window dresser we used to know last autumn in the basement.'

'How do you like that!' she exclaimed. 'Francis! You are a secretive girl. But, Julia, what have you done with your little tailor?'

'Nothing in particular,' said Julia, blushing. 'The fact is that I am not really capable of dealing with one affair, let alone two.'

'One at a time is enough for me also,' said Edith. 'I'm involved to the crown of my head with Archie, fighting for my very existence. What would you say, Julia, if I told you that at this very moment Archie is waiting for me in the lounge of the Piccadilly Hotel while I am here, talking to you, and feeling more and more miserable because I haven't the guts to go to him!'

'No!' exclaimed Julia. 'No! But I, I just can't understand. He'll be furious!'

'So furious that he will break it off. Or so unhappy that . . . Oh Julia, darling. There is no solution either way. Of course I have no right to let him wait for me all the evening at the Piccadilly Hotel. But supposing I were to go and he were to ask me the question he is bound to ask me, what am I going to say? It is not that I have a guilt complex. If I erred it was through love and trust and I've paid for it a thousand times. All by myself, Julia, with nobody to hold my hand. But all the same, though I'm in the clear in my own eyes, I am not the girl Archie believes I am. So what am I going to do about it?'

Julia looked at her, trying to find the right answer.

'Perhaps . . . ?' she started.

'No,' said Edith. 'Don't say anything. You haven't enough experience. You might give me the wrong advice. I shall leave Archie kicking his heels while I take a cab and go to my aunt's place. She and you are the only people in the world I can trust. I am going to ask her what to do.'

Julia said: 'It's terrible to imagine Archie pacing up and

down the foyer of the Piccadilly. I feel sorry for him. Meanwhile, wish me luck for tomorrow night!'

'What a pair we make!' said Edith, laughing. 'You afraid of finding yourself tongue-tied with Francis; I afraid of saying too much to Archie!'

Outside the Plaza the two girls hesitated a moment. Then Edith kissed Julia lightly on the forehead, hailed a passing taxi and was gone.

Julia crossed the Haymarket, cut down Panton Street and made her way across Leicester Square. Summer with its yellowed grass and dusty evenings would soon be over, and the leaves would start to fall off the London plane trees. A group of youths had gathered outside a shop where they sold gramophone records. Julia felt secretly hurt because not one of them looked at her. Was it because she had forgotten to make up her eyes, or were they not interested in girls?

She had no sooner crossed Cambridge Circus and reached the top of her own street than she saw, in a short-sighted blur, Iris saying goodbye to the young doctor, who was already in his car. Before she could reach them Iris had gone back into the house, closing the front door behind her and the doctor had started the car and was moving off. She would ask her mother what news there was of Iris's mother, but already her mind had reverted to the coat her mother was making for her and she hoped it would be ready for a fitting. The buttons were in her handbag. Her heart always started to beat with excitement at the thought of something new to wear, and in her almost childish imagination a new coat transformed itself into a chariot to take her over the chimney tops and far away. But why did she always have to wait so long? Why could not her mother, like the little tailor in the fairy story, cut and prepare the coat, fall asleep and find it all ready for her daughter when she woke up? It was, of course, the lure of ready-to-wear all over again.

It would be unwise for her, Julia reflected, to count on the coat being ready for a fitting. No! When she arrived home, panting and eager, she would see the coat suspended from a hanger, one sleeve in, the other not yet in place. There would be a gaping hole. Why? Because during the morning or the afternoon Miss Pauline, or perhaps her mother's elegant customer from Maddox Street, would have been round to order something new for themselves. They would, of course, have seen Julia's half-finished red coat. 'What is that?' they would ask. 'Who are you making the red coat for?' Her mother was far too experienced to tell them it was for Julia. 'I have a new customer,' she would say archly. 'An extremely elegant young person.' In the past, before she had learnt to resort to such stratagems, her customers had often accused her of working better for her daughter than for them, which in fact was not true. Indeed the reverse may have been the case because Julia was always too impatient for her mother to have time to deal properly with the finishing off. There was also the fact that Julia was in the full bloom of her innocent youth and whatever she wore looked well on her!

When Julia arrived home, her mother was indeed working on her coat. Julia flew to embrace her, but even as her lips brushed against her mother's fair hair she saw the box of chocolates on the worktable.

'Miss Pauline has been here!' she exclaimed as if her mother had done something wrong.

'Yes,' said her mother with a twinkle in her eye. 'Miss Pauline came but she did not order anything. On the contrary, she asked me to make a slight alteration in a dress she had bought from one of her customers. As she was in a hurry, I charged her nearly as much as I would have done for making her a new dress, and because the alteration was relatively simple, and there was not much unpicking to do, I finished the whole job before lunch. She was delighted because she had kept it for the last two months in her wardrobe, afraid to bring it to me. How do I know this? Because certain materials are apt to smell of mildew after being boxed up for a time, and this was a cheap dress that she had been a fool to buy in the first place. I charged her more than twice what the alteration was worth, but she needed that dress. She feels she simply must wear something different every day to impress the girls who work under her. All women in executive positions are like that!'

'I am sure Mrs Davies isn't like that,' thought Julia. 'I would not imagine she needs to impress Betty and me! She might, on the other hand, want to impress Edith's buyer, or the buyer of the stockings and handbags department, or the beautician in Perfumery.' Materials had a male chief who had been chosen not only on account of his experience in this difficult matter but also, she supposed, because of his good looks. Whenever any of his assistants had difficulty in completing an important sale they invariably ran off to fetch him so that he could bring his sex appeal to bear on the wavering customer. The entire store revolved on beauty and charm in the same way as love was supposed to make the world itself go round. When people cease to make use of charm, thought Julia, there will be no fun left in buying and selling.

Seeing that her red coat really was making progress now under her mother's deft fingers, Julia put her arms round her neck and kissed her a second time.

'I stayed talking to Edith for a while in the foyer of the Plaza,' she said. 'She has a terrible problem.'

'Of that I have no doubt,' said her mother. 'Next time you bring her home you should tell her fortune in the cards. It will give her something else to think about. In spite of the fact that one knows very well that all that sort of thing is nonsense, one goes on doing it. When I'm alone, for instance, in the middle of the day, and I begin to feel depressed, I play a game of Patience and it is amazing how much better I feel afterwards if it comes out right.'

'It's my future you need to tell,' said Julia. 'I have been invited out to supper by a young man tomorrow night.'

There! The great news was out! Julia looked up quickly, nervously, to catch the first sign of her mother's reaction. To her surprise, it was one of intense interest, and her first words were: 'What are you going to wear?'

'My new jersey with the coloured stripes and my pleated skirt,' said Julia, who had already made up her mind. 'I want to feel at ease, and a jumper and skirt are more informal than a dress. They won't make me look as if I expected him to give me an expensive meal. If I bore him, or he bores me, I can jump on a bus and come straight home. A pleated skirt is the ideal thing. This does not prevent you, Mother, from telling my fortune in that old pack of cards amongst your needles and pins.'

Miss Pauline and the woman from Maddox Street seldom left their dressmaker's flat without asking her to foretell their future. Curiously enough, though Julia's mother had referred to it as nonsense, both mother and daughter had this extraordinary inherited gift that, on occasion, allowed them to reach the most remarkable results. So much so that they were both a little afraid of it. The inspiration could, of course, be padded out if need be with cunning, so that in the end it was hard to know what was true and what was not. Enough of the extraordinary remained, however, to make the telling of the cards something almost magic. When the woman from Maddox Street peered into her cards she invariably found a multitude of kings and jacks, but then this was only to be expected in a woman who had as many men in her life as the old woman had children in her shoe. But Julia's mother was astute. She wanted to find out certain things about the woman from Maddox Street that her client appeared unwilling to tell her. Julia's mother, for instance, had always had a strange presentiment that the woman from Maddox Street had a mother of her own tucked away somewhere. She therefore embodied her, so to speak, in the guise of the Queen of Spades, a widow or possibly an abandoned wife. Upon being faced with this apparition, the woman from Maddox Street said nothing, which was tantamount to admitting that Julia's mother had struck right. Thus was the beginning of knowledge! Of women like the one from Maddox Street, Julia's mother used to say: 'Their qualities and defects are surprisingly interwoven like the leaves of an artichoke, lies, generosity, pride, vanity, all shielding a soft, loyal core.'

She now said to her daughter:

'Wake up, Julia. Cut the cards with your left hand.'

The game proved very disappointing. Nothing exciting turned up—only a knave of diamonds, which is not good, and a knave of spades, which is worse. The knave of hearts remained in hiding.

Julia's mother said:

'At least, my dear, you won't get a swollen head!'

Julia's answering laugh was a trifle forced. She would get her clothes ready, and if Francis took her to supper in a different part of London from the one in which she lived, she would at least get that out of it. She could also brag a bit to Betty, or even say, as Betty often said when things went wrong for her: 'There are plenty of other fish in the sea!'

Was it Julia's imagination or had she never seen Regent Street so crowded, the store so full of women evidently from all parts of the world, enchanted to find themselves in this bright, golden, feminine atmosphere. The chase from department to department, for ribbons and scarves, for gloves and handbags, for perfume and face powder, or hand-made French lingerie and fantastically beautiful dresses to change one's personality, was like some continual ballet. The cashier, for whom this summer was proving a strain, gave the impression that what was left of her youth was being annihilated by cascades of coins and grubby paper money that somebody from another world would have thought of as being the very antithesis of all the beautiful things for which it was so unwillingly exchanged. Julia, who had been run off her feet (the girls on the ground floor were not allowed to sit down between sales), judged that her commission would not be too bad at the end of the month. The last few days invariably raised speculation on this score. The end of the month bonus, being unknown, added salt to the dreariness of a girl's basic salary, and for

198

this reason was popular amongst those who possessed the adventurous or gambling spirit. At seventeen, however, it is sad to spend so much time in every month wanting to grow older in order to reach out for a sum so pathetically inadequate to a girl's needs.

Julia's hair was not enjoying one of its better days. Her hair was a multi-seasoned barometer which in spite of vigorous brushing had good days, fair days and downright bad days—days when she felt that she simply could not do anything with it. Fortunately in the eyes of the beholder it never looked different. She said to herself: 'I am taking this date altogether too seriously. I am eaten up with pride. What I am trying to do is to make an enormous impression on him—and he is just not worth it!'

Like her assistant, Betty had been kept so busy all day that when the closing bell rang she was bursting with a great desire to talk, as her expression showed. This was a pity because it was the evening of all evenings when Julia's mind was elsewhere. Betty, who never noticed anything, exclaimed in her friendliest tone:

'I have nothing to do this evening and I don't feel like going straight home. What would you say to us two going to the pictures?'

'Not tonight, Betty. I have a date.'

Betty's expression hardened. Her assistant had suddenly made her feel cheap. Had she known that Julia was engaged she would have pretended to have had something important to do herself. She snapped too quickly:

'You might have told me! Who is it with? With Edith, I suppose?'

'No, not with Edith. With a boy you may have seen. He works here.'

'Oh! It's a "him"!' said Betty, turning petulantly on her heels.

Julia hurried out into Regent Street. On the next corner, as he had promised, stood Francis—but he was not alone! Beside him was the girl from the General Office.

'Hello!' said the girl, smiling, as Julia advanced. 'You have no idea how we missed you down in the basement— you and your cheery girl-friend. I hear that you are both doing splendidly. I hope you won't mind me sharing Francis for five minutes. He drives me whenever he can to catch my train at Charing Cross Station. Thanks to his kindness I get home an hour earlier than I would otherwise. Hurry, Francis! It won't wait for me, you know.'

The two girls, both in jerseys and pleated skirts, followed Francis to his car and, as they drove towards Piccadilly Circus, the girl from the General Office said:

'Did Francis tell you, Julia, that I finish at the end of this month? I am going to be married!'

'Oh! I am so glad for you!' exclaimed Julia.

'My fiancé works in one of the big banks,' she said. 'He has been appointed manager in an overseas branch. I am terribly happy.'

'Where?' asked Julia.

'In South America. I'm already learning Spanish. Isn't it exciting?'

Edith was right, thought Julia. The girls from the General Office have their lives mapped out for them as if on ruled paper. She will have a house of her own in some beautiful, romantic climate. She will be somebody in the foreign colony. She will come back in six or seven years to England and by that time her parents will be ready to give them their beautiful house in Kent. There was always this slight bitterness in Julia's heart because of the difference between her position and that of some other girls. Yet she was pleased for this particular girl whom she had known from her first day at the store and who had managed her affairs so much better than Daisy had managed hers. This was the chasm between failure and success.

In the courtyard of Charing Cross Station, the young fiancée jumped lightly out of the car and waved goodbye. She threw a kiss to Julia.

'She is much sweeter than I guessed,' said Julia.

She and Francis sat side by side in the comfortable

leather seats, and after a moment Francis asked: 'What would you like to do?'

The traffic was beginning to die down in the Strand. Soon people would be going to the theatre, driving to the Savoy for supper in the grill-room or dancing in the restaurant. There would be cocktails and banquets in the various suites overlooking the Embankment and the river.

'What would you like to do?' Francis repeated.

'I would like to be taken along there,' said Julia, pointing along the Strand. 'Past Fleet Street to St Paul's Cathedral.'

Francis laughed. This was not at all the request he had expected from a girl and it puzzled him. He had imagined that she would choose some fashionable restaurant, or perhaps ask to go dancing. Dancing bored him and he said:

'What a wonderful idea for a summer evening.'

But as he drove slowly past the Adelphi Theatre he asked:

'Why St Paul's specially? I mean, is there a reason?'

'Why, yes,' she answered, 'because of the Plague.'

'The what?' he asked. They were passing Southampton Street, and this explanation in her unassuming little voice, as she demurely patted the pleats of her skirt, nearly made him swerve into the evening-paper seller.

'Because of Harrison Ainsworth and Defoe,' she said. 'We read them aloud. Mother has a passion for churchyards and gravestones.'

'Heavens!' he exclaimed. 'You are a strange little creature. From our morning sessions in the store basement, where you sat giggling with your dark-haired girl-friend, I never pictured you'd be so ghoulish. Still, to St Paul's we shall go. It's not the same St Paul's. I imagine you are aware of that?'

'It doesn't matter,' she said.

They passed the church of the 'oranges and lemons', the Law Courts and so along Fleet Street and slowly up Ludgate Hill while the golden evening light fell on the dome of St Paul's, but when they reached the forecourt she said: 'May we go on?'

'Of course we may go on.'

'It's so restful in the car after the bustle in the streets.'

'We will take our history lesson comfortably seated,' he said.

He took her to the Monument, told her what it was all about and then down to the wharves of Billingsgate, smelling of fish, and so to the sudden glory of the Tower.

She had never seen it before. Her tiny shriek of delight gave him more pleasure than if she had leapt up and kissed him. He was appallingly shy with girls. He never quite knew how to amuse them. He asked her out because she was exceptional and put him at his ease:

'What does this make you dream of? Your fate if like Anne Boleyn you had married Henry the Eighth?'

She laughed.

'Do you want us to see if it's open? If we can visit the Crown Jewels or something?'

'No,' she said. 'Let's go on.'

'Go on where?'

'Across Tower Bridge and back again.'

Francis leant back in the driving seat and relaxed. He had been afraid of involving himself with this girl, and the fact that she was revealing herself to be so gentle and understanding diminished the risk of eventual involvement. He was still determined to put his career, his fierce ambition for attaining some small degree of personal success, before marriage, and it struck him that this girl, like the one from the General Office, who all along had been engaged to another man, had perhaps no more designs on him than he had on her. She was pleasant, pretty and, in spite of her talk about St Paul's, no more intelligent than the average girl. Clever girls were nearly always a bore. Suppose he drove her back by way of Southwark to Blackfriars Bridge. He could tell her about Shakespeare's Globe Theatre. She probably would not listen. The drone of the engine was making her drowsy. What lovely golden hair she had, and whatever perfume she used smelt quite delicious. If he had not been so shy, so absolutely determined not to get involved with any girl, he would have stopped the car and buried his face in that beautiful golden hair!

Here they were in the middle of Blackfriars Bridge; it was nearly eight o'clock.

'You must be famished!' said Francis with a feeling of guilt. This was being downright rude. He had invited a girl to dinner and had offered her nothing to eat.

'I am never hungry when I am interested,' said Julia in her little-girl voice. The words were scarcely out than she felt as hungry as a tigress.

'I am hungry!' said Francis. 'Let us drive to Chelsea all along the Embankment. Would you like that?'

'I can't think of anything more wonderful!' exclaimed Julia.

So they sped along the Embankment as far as Westminster, past the Houses of Parliament and back to the water again. He took her to a famous pub where he helped her choose her chop, gave it to the chef to grill while they drank bitter in a tankard. Julia lost her shyness. She talked about her mother, she talked about Edith. Francis looked at this slip of a girl with amusement and wonder. What ingenuousness! Her laughter was so infectious that it exploded like a catherine wheel all round the pub with its crowded bar, its little white linen covered tables, its atmosphere thick with acrid tobacco smoke.

Soon after eleven, when he dropped her at the corner of the street just as the lights of the Palace Theatre were going out, she sprang out of the car as lightly as a London sparrow.

'Don't bang the car door shut!' she whispered, pushing it gently. 'I don't want to wake Mother.'

She smiled at him and was gone before he even had time to ask himself if he should have kissed her or not!

Betty did her best the next day to question Julia closely about her date with Francis, but as Julia had already recounted the details to her mother over breakfast, she was not inclined to go over them a second time. Betty therefore relapsed into a monologue about her parents against whom she had mounting grievances. When Julia went over to greet the cashier, she told her she had left her husband in bed with a feverish cold and she looked forward to only one thing, the end of the working day so that she could hurry back and look after him. As their telephone was at the end of a draughty hall and she had implored him not to leave his room, where she had lit the gas fire, she would not even have the satisfaction of being able to telephone. A neighbour had promised to bring him a bowl of soup and look in once or twice during the day. 'I worry about him,' she said, 'because he runs a high temperature with the slightest chill and it goes to his lungs. Our son is just the same. Fortunately I never have the time to be ill, and I hope it goes on that way until we have finished paying for the house.'

Back in her own department, Julia found a junior from the dress department with a note from Edith. She read: 'Wait for me tonight without fail. Important.' She had signed it with a tiny red heart drawn with her lipstick. While Julia was reading the note the junior walked on tiptoe round the garden of artificial flowers which, like so many real ones, had no scent. But she obviously admired them, for her eyes were full of wonderful dreams.

Waiting for Edith that evening in the passage leading into Regent Street Julia saw Francis hurrying out of the staff entrance, but before he had time to see her she had stepped quickly back into the shadow of a doorway. She was anxious not to look as if she were waiting for him. Her instinct was a happy one, for a moment later a woman laden with parcels detached herself from the crowd and greeted him. Julia wondered if she was his mother.

Edith, as was her custom, came up from behind her and made her jump. The affectionate warmth of Edith's arrival and the wonderful, deep laugh, always surprised her. 'Let's go to the Corner House,' Edith announced, linking arms and leading her in the direction of Piccadilly Circus. 'I promised to buy a pound of assorted sweets for our new junior who is trying to give up smoking.'

Julia was anxious to hear Edith's story from the time the two girls had parted outside the Plaza. She wanted to know what had happened to the unfortunate Archie who, in her imagination, had spent so much of the evening miserably pacing up and down the foyer of the Piccadilly Hotel. She also wanted to know what advice, if any, Edith's aunt had given her regarding her painful dilemma. But though Edith never tried to keep secrets from her friend it was not her habit usually to take up threads at the exact point at which they needed picking up. So Julia was obliged to let her talk at random, knowing that an untimely interruption could put a sudden end to the confidence. Edith said:

'Oh, yes, he telephoned. The business of waiting at the Piccadilly Hotel had nothing of particular interest about it. Either I was worth waiting for, or I was not. Besides, it does not mean that because a man enjoys a girl's company he wants to marry her. There was not any suggestion of my being engaged. Nor is there now. I have ceased to be one of those girls who believe that just because one goes out a few times with a man anything is going to come of it. Have I seen him again? Is that what you want to know? Why, yes, I have seen him several times. Not only that, I have been quite often to Regent's Park, and it is because of that, I mean because of Regent's Park, that my own dilemma, which prevented me from meeting him that evening at the Piccadilly Hotel, has become less delicate.'

'I'm not sure I understand,' said Julia.

'I don't want you to understand, except perhaps partially. I don't understand everything myself. It would be absurd to try to set everything out like a mathematical formula. To pretend that you can give a reason for this or for that. I hate searching for reasons. The mere fact of seeking a reason destroys its reason to exist. Anyway, as I tell you I went back to Regent's Park, to Laura's house. See! I am now calling his sister by her Christian name. Nothing can prove more explicitly that we have become friends and that I have had plenty of opportunity to become part of Laura's family—if indeed you can call hers a family!'

'What on earth do you mean, Edith? It sounded such a happy house!'

'Yes, it did. I mean that it struck me in that way when I went there for dinner on that first evening when we dropped you at the Palace Theatre. In a way it was. The house had a great many of the things that would make any girl happy—me or you, for that matter. Or your mother. Enough money, beautiful linen, real silver cutlery, lovely carpets and lamps, beautiful rooms, an expensive car waiting at the porch and some lovely children in the nursery. Imagine what luxury this would mean for your mother who has to make do in a tiny flat with never enough money? And that Norwegian girl. Do you remember me telling you about her? Pretty, clever, young, polite, herself of an excellent family. Fun to have with one and about the house. In all these different ways it is a happy house. Or at least it should be. Only there is this one terrible thing. Laura's husband does not love her any more. Or to be exact—for what does love mean anyway?—he wants to go off with another woman, a girl of twenty-two who already has a child. That is what makes it an unhappy house.'

'It does not seem fair,' said Julia, thinking of Laura's husband, 'that with all those advantages he should make Laura unhappy. As you say Mother and I would be happy with a quarter as many.'

'If you think that having advantages necessarily makes one happy,' said Edith.

'I shouldn't worry too much about Laura,' said Julia, trying to appear sophisticated and worldly. 'Most novels contain a husband who threatens to leave home at one stage of the proceedings. It's a classic situation. Often they think twice about it, especially if there are children. Laura has a strong hand to play. Did you not tell me there were two lovely little girls, the elder about ten?'

'It is they who are responsible for the situation becoming serious,' said Edith.

'Those sweet children? Why?'

'According to Archie,' said Edith, 'both Laura and her

husband never stop giving them presents, dolls, sewing tables, musical instruments, gramophone records, everything. It is the modern idea, to give the children even more than they know what to do with. The latest was a model theatre. The younger girl wants to be an actress and recites verses; the older one dreams of being a ballet dancer. Laura and the two girls were playing theatre the day after my visit when, according to Archie, their father came back from one of his periodic absences and started having words with Laura. Of course the first thing she did was to send the children up to their own room. She apparently said to them: "Now girls, go and read for a while. I'll call you when tea is ready."

'But instead of going to the nursery the two girls listened at the door and so they heard a violent scene between their parents. In the course of this Laura accused their father of having a mistress, and he threatened to go off and live with her! The younger of the two little girls went into hysterics and the parents had to telephone for their doctor.'

'Oh!' cried Julia. 'What a dreadful thing to happen!'

'Laura is thirty,' said Edith. 'She was so lovely that first evening I saw her. Such a beautiful, dignified hostess at dinner—and then later when she came down in her fur coat, waiting for her escort to lead her to his car. Her life has become so appalling that when I compare my own load of troubles with the ones she has to bear, I start wondering which of us deserves the most pity—she for unhappiness over a broken marriage, or I for one that can never start.'

'What is happening to Laura is tragic,' said Julia, 'but it does not directly concern you.'

'Of course it concerns me,' said Edith, 'because it affects Archie. You must try to understand. Archie is young and very spoilt by life, and he's still full of principles and prejudices. Pain and disappointment have not yet made him tender and forgiving. He never imagined that such a thing could happen in his own family, to his sister. He has been hit almost as hard as she has. Archie is not quite the same carefree, assured young man that he was on the evening he dropped you off at the Palace Theatre. When we go back to the house in Regent's Park, even the Norwegian girl does not laugh over nothing as she used to, and the little girls cling to their mother and even to Archie as if they were afraid to lose them too.'

'It must be awful for you,' said Julia.

'Yes, but not for the reason you think,' said Edith as they turned into the Corner House and made their way through the crowds on the ground floor, milling round stands of cold meat, pastries, fruit and flowers.

'Here is what you are looking for!' exclaimed Julia, pointing to a veritable wall of multi-coloured boiled sweets. 'If not for the reason I think, for what reason?' she asked.

'I have the impression that the family needs me,' said Edith. 'Laura is affectionate, and the little girls treat me as if I were their elder sister. I have never known that sort of affection before. My real sister and I were always distant from each other. The fact is that, as far as I know, she has never tried to get into touch with me. We have become strangers. But the two little girls in Regent's Park are such darlings that they want and need my presence. Oh, Julia, can you not understand the inevitable result? I feel a fraud. It is as if I had introduced myself into their midst by false pretences. Imagine my plight when they find me out! They will throw me out, like some girl who might have broken into the house to steal the silver.'

'You exaggerate,' said Julia. 'People just don't think that way any longer. They are more broad-minded.'

'Don't you believe it,' said Edith. 'Let us go and have a coffee.'

They found two vacant seats at a narrow table and when the coffee came Edith piled lumps of sugar unthinkingly into it. She put in so many that the black liquid overflowed messily into the saucer.

'Do you suppose I could bring bad luck to people?' she asked.

Julia had hoped to talk to her about her own experiences with Francis, but this was not the moment to do so. Edith, like everybody else, both in happiness and unhappiness, wanted only to think about herself. She did not seek a shoulder to cry on, not even the satisfaction of moral support—only the immense relief of being able to talk herself to a standstill. Apart from that, Edith was mistress of her destiny, and she was sufficiently worldly wise to be aware how little she mattered to anybody, except perhaps to Julia, and that she must fight alone. She must fight all out with pointed nails because otherwise she ran a big risk of being crushed by an unjust fate at this precise moment when she was emerging from the past.

Edith told herself that she had tried loyally not to encourage Archie. She had purposely skipped his dates, made a fool of him, notably that evening at the Piccadilly Hotel, and had told her junior in the dress department on more than one occasion to say when he telephoned that she was out or engaged with a customer. What she could not help, what made a rather special link between them, was their common love of hard work. Archie was a fiend for work, just as she was. Though he was born to relative ease, there was nothing of the playboy about him. He took his work at the office seriously and there was no doubt at all that unless something entirely unexpected happened, like a take-over, he would succeed his father as head of the business. He was beginning to take Edith into his confidence more than in her opinion he was justified in doing. He had pointed out, though it really did not need pointing out at all, that if something went badly wrong with Laura's marriage and if, though it hardly bore thinking about, she was obliged to sell the house in Regent's Park, then she and the two little girls would need Archie's active help. That would add, of course, to his worries and responsibilities.

'But of course,' said Edith, continuing this line of thought aloud, 'Archie's parents, for all I know, may have some rich banker's daughter all lined up for him! He has never even breathed the suggestion of marriage.'

Julia reflected that the lady from Maddox Street was fortunate indeed never to find herself in a position of having to do any explaining to a man. If one did have to do any awkward explaining, she felt, it would be easier to do it to another woman. Women would more easily understand.

But on further reflection she fell to asking herself why Edith felt this desperate necessity to explain anything at all. Daisy took the diametrically opposite view. Daisy said concerning her own troubles: 'I will deny everything!' and she had made it clear that if a neighbour, or anybody else for that matter, so much as hinted at anything she would immediately have her solicitor issue a writ for slander. Perhaps she was right? What good was it to live in an emancipated society if one did not allow oneself an occasional mistake? Had not both of them, Edith especially, fully paid for what they had done?

But Edith, divining Julia's thought, said aloud: 'What is the good of living in the modern world if it is not in one's nature to take advantage of it?'

'You never told me,' said Julia suddenly, 'if you found your aunt at home the other evening and what advice she gave you?'

'My aunt was at home all right,' said Edith, 'but she had company—women of her own and my mother's generation, well-to-do women, their hair styled and tinted by fashionable West End hairdressers, their hands manicured and be-ringed, wearing good models like the ones I sell at the store but designed for girls of eighteen. Aunt's friends rather sickened me, and looking at them I couldn't help thinking that nuns in their medieval dress are the only ones of our sex who remain eternally youthful by the elegance of what they wear.

'On the other hand, there were excellent things to eat, Russian caviar on hot toast and expensive *petits fours*. Aunt is particular about what she gives to her friends. There were French château-bottled wines and champagne for those who preferred it. I ate and drank with pleasure for I was hungry, and from time to time my aunt shot a quick glance of such real affection at me that I almost loved her. I had the impression of having rediscovered the satisfaction of belonging to a family—in spite of my own reluctance. Mind, I think it worked both ways. If I was pleased to belong to her, I feel sure she was just as happy to point me out as her dear niece. She felt that I enriched her new flat. So I sat down in a very comfortable armchair and felt, yes, Julia, I really did feel as if I were to some extent at home. Sitting in my own chair at home.

'It was precisely this feeling that, unconsciously, I had been in need of. I had intended to ask advice, but unwittingly she gave me something much more precious, a feeling of belonging-ness. Of course, I may have slightly exaggerated this feeling because of the champagne, the caviar and the armchair. I don't say that she would necessarily come to my help in a serious emergency, though even that is possible, but the mere fact that she is there and wants me is an enriching feeling.

'She approves of me because I am doing well at the store. She has the good sense to recognize in me the right material for a successful career girl—hard work, ambition, good looks and a highly developed dress sense. These qualities make me a decorative and desirable niece. When I walk into her drawing-room she looks up in pleasure. If I were not so tormented by my involvement with Archie, and now with Archie's sister Laura as well, I might attach myself to my aunt and become something like an adopted daughter.'

'You mean you could go and live with her?'

'I am not sure. Sharing a flat with other girls of one's own age can be tremendous fun, and I'm not willing to take so important a decision at the moment. We fight and quarrel, but we have a common denominator in our youth. Agnes has brought in a new girl who sleeps on a camp bed in the living-room for the time being. She is an absolute beauty, not yet nineteen. Agnes herself is engaged to a Danish boy and as soon as they are married they are going to live in Copenhagen. She has done very well for herself, and if ever we go to Denmark she has invited us to go and stay with her.'

The two girls paid the bill and went out into Coventry

Street. It was a warm evening in early September and they were glad to be in each other's company and to follow the crowd that moved slowly in the direction of Leicester Square. This was their London and they loved every trodden inch of it. Edith, happy to have so fully discussed her own problems, said:

'My buyer is disposing of a number of dresses before the start of the autumn season. If it were not for your mother's thing against ready-made models, it might have been worth your while to come up. There is a little navy-blue model that is absolutely "you", and as it is practically being given away I have put it aside for you. Perhaps you could tell your mother I had given it to you? It wouldn't be much of a lie!'

'I don't need to lie to her!' said Julia stoutly. 'I would love the dress. When can I have it?'

The idea of having a dress specially chosen for her by Edith was delightful. Her confidence in Edith's good taste was complete. 'When can I have it?' she repeatedly asked as they crossed over to the south side of Leicester Square.

Glad to see how warmly her gesture had been accepted, Edith said:

'Tomorrow night.'

Skirting the wall of the National Portrait Gallery, they emerged into Trafalgar Square where Edith would take the tube. Facing the steps and the pillared entrance to the National Gallery, their backs to the church of St Martin-in-the-Fields, Edith asked:

'Have you ever been in the National Gallery?'

'Yes,' said Julia. 'After I got the sack from the draper's shop. I went inside to think things out, to decide how I was going to break the news to Mother. It was warm and pleasant and the pictures helped me to put things in their right perspective. Since then I go in whenever I want to be alone to think. Of course, to come back to the draper's shop, the good thing about Mother is that she always took my side even when it was my fault.'

'What did you do at the draper's shop?' asked Edith.

'I was a secretary but a bad one. I am rather good at spelling and my English is not too bad, but I never could read my shorthand back. Though I must admit that now I don't need it professionally I am constantly making use of it to jot down notes. Notes for my own use, of course. However, I am not like you. I never was cut out to be a career girl. The store is better than an office because at least when I collect my commission money at the end of the month I have this little extra to show to what extent I have pulled my weight. I rather like selling things, but I terribly wish the right man would come along. I don't think girls were made to work—I mean, not for long!'

Edith laughed.

'Imagine what would have happened to me when I arrived in London without any money if I hadn't been able to carve out a place for myself! Oh, it's lovely that girls can do so much! Such different things! And what would happen to your mother without you to help her pay the rent?'

'Shall we meet during the lunch hour tomorrow?' asked Julia.

'Yes,' said Edith, 'at Umberto's, at the usual time. The first to arrive waits for the other. Cheerio!'

'Cheerio!' said Julia, turning on her heels to return home by way of Charing Cross Road.

Her mother was waiting with pinched lips. 'Julia comes home later every night,' she thought as her daughter came rushing into the room.

'If you burn the candle at both ends . . .' she began, 'you will fall ill, and then where shall we be?'

There was nothing that Julia could answer to this except that perhaps she felt the same way about her mother when, as so often happened, she saw her stitching away at a client's dress until nearly midnight. On the whole they were rather ridiculous with their constant preoccupation with each other's health. Mother and daughter—this fragile, irreplaceable relationship!

Next day when Julia arrived at the café Edith had not yet made an appearance. Umberto looked distraught. His eyes were bloodshot, his features drawn. His little wife Lydia was not to be seen.

'Where is Lydia?' asked Julia as soon as Umberto came to her table.

'At the Middlesex,' he said. 'We have a baby boy!'

'Oh!' cried Julia. 'What simply wonderful news!'

She plied him with questions, asking at what time of the night she had been delivered and how much the baby weighed and how the mother had come through the ordeal. 'Well,' said Umberto proudly, 'but it is I who now feel the strain. I can scarcely keep awake!'

'A boy!' repeated Julia. 'What are you going to call him?'

'Lydia wants to call him Charles. My wife is English, you know, and I—well, this country has given me everything I treasure most—my wife, my business and now my son!'

While they were talking, Edith came in.

'Lydia has given birth to a baby boy at the Middlesex,' said Julia, 'and they are going to call him Charles!'

Edith's eyes filled with tears.

'Oh!' she cried, embracing Umberto. 'I am so happy for you. Julia and I will go to see Lydia during visiting hours at the Middlesex tonight.'

The idea of Lydia's baby had altogether upset her. Too many memories came pouring into her head. The bun she had ordered with her coffee remained uneaten on her plate. She said to Julia:

'We will take a taxi immediately after work. I will pay.'

Julia loved babies and was delighted at the thought of going to see Lydia at the Middlesex, but she had less reason than Edith to allow the news to shatter her youthful spirits. As she ate Edith's unwanted bun she reflected that this would be the second night running that she would arrive home late. Her mother would be once more in a state of alarm. What a pity there was no telephone.

'I hope they will allow us to see the baby!' said Edith.

Julia was puzzled: 'Have you no date with Archie?' she asked.

'No,' said Edith, 'he is sitting for some law or accounting examination. I am not sure which. It appears that a university degree is not enough.'

In Julia's opinion, Edith had never looked prettier. Her air of docile resignation at the thought that Archie's examinations took precedence over their evening date added softness to her expression. It was already wifely, proprietory, maternal. However, the thought of Lydia's baby remained paramount in her mind. She said, by a rapid association of ideas:

'I wonder what my young sister looks like now that she is a grown woman! Do you suppose there is a baby on the way?'

'Will you go to see her one day?' asked Julia. 'Or will you wait until she decides to come to London and see you?'

'I have been asking myself the same question,' said Edith, whose bitterness of their basement days was now undergoing a change.

'Do you suppose your aunt has told her that you and she are reunited?'

'Possibly. Aunt can do as she pleases. There is a time for everything. Only the other day Archie asked me if I planned to go home for Christmas. It was the first time he has asked me about my family. Until now he appeared to take them for granted, and merely talked about his own. I like listening to him. I doubt if I have ever done so much listening before. I have so much talking to do during the day, trying to sell dresses to women, that to listen all evening to a man is a restful change. Doing the talking myself is not only an embarrassment but it teaches me nothing. There is very little a girl can teach a man. She is much wiser to look intelligent and listen. His parents have a house with a big garden, almost a small park, I gather, and only one gardener to look after it. The set-up is alarmingly similar to that of my first love. I just wonder if there is something about me that attracts the same sort of boy. There are so many questions I keep turning over in my mind, and the one concerning my own family is not the least painful. I thought I could wrench it out of my life, like a weed out of the garden, but it comes back stronger every time. I envy you, Julia, having this old-fashioned docility towards your mother.'

That evening, when Julia came into Regent Street and looked about quickly for Edith, she found her with a girl she guessed was her new junior, though the girl almost immediately waved goodbye and melted into the crowd.

'I bought some things for Lydia on my way back from lunch,' said Julia, falling into step with her friend as they hurried off. 'A few chocolates and some white baby wool which seemed the best thing. She can knit another garment while she is in hospital.'

They planned to walk to the far side of Oxford Street before taking a taxi, but in fact they went even farther, not wanting to find themselves sitting in a traffic block. Close together, perched on their high heels, taking quick, short steps, they remained silent for a while. Julia was on the point of showing her companion the little club where she and Iris went dancing, but suddenly she restrained herself from doing so as if anxious to keep it a secret. The idea of keeping something secret even from her closest friend had a strange appeal.

Edith now hailed a passing cab so that they should at least arrive fresh at the hospital. When they gave the address to the driver, he exclaimed: 'Fancy you girls going there. I have just come from the hospital!'

In fact they had left the hiring of the cab so late that it was barely worth taking it. While Edith paid the fare, Julia bought a bunch of Parma violets from the flower seller at the gates and, after asking their way, the two girls went straight up to the maternity ward.

Lydia, in a cloud of pink silk, was sitting up in bed with an excited group of girls round her. Happiness and pride made her almost beautiful. Edith and Julia, surprised and somewhat disconcerted to see the young mother surrounded by admirers, kissed her, presented their gifts and looked round shyly in the hope of seeing the baby. However, the baby was not visible and, after reiterated congratulations and an exchange of commonplaces, the two girls took their leave.

For some reason that they found difficult to express in words, the visit had proved a failure; the expedition that they had looked forward to as a marvellous adventure left them with a sense of regret and even bitterness. The hospital, the maternity ward, the aggressive happiness of the young mother had plunged Edith back into a sense of remorse and, as they walked briskly towards Oxford Street, she had obvious difficulty in holding back her tears. She would have preferred to be alone, somewhere away from the noise and the bustle of the town, free to bury her face in the crook of an arm and weep her heart out. Julia, whose only disappointment had been not to have the fun of looking down into the features of a newly born baby, was sufficiently sensitive to guess what was passing in Edith's mind, but she lacked the experience to say so and to comfort her. She said:

'Here is my bus stop. Would you mind if I left you and hurried home? I am afraid mother is going to be furious.'

'That's all right,' said Edith without looking up.

When Julia's mother learnt the reason for her daughter's lateness, she forebore to blame her, appeared interested in the hospital but regretted that Julia had not seen the baby.

'Edith seems very unhappy,' said Julia. 'Her true love runs far from smooth!'

'You do not surprise me,' said her mother. 'Love affairs for a pretty girl are five a penny, but true love is rare, about as rare as finding the proverbial needle in the haystack. Yet your friend Edith is a beauty and, when she wants to, can be as gay as a humming bird. Gaiety for a girl is nearly as vital as beauty. A girl who can make a man laugh starts off with an immense advantage. Edith is also intelligent in a useful, worldly way; though cleverness is not all that useful for a girl and as everybody knows it must not show. You and she are two girls who have got almost everything for success. The trouble is that few of us get what we merit. Perhaps we women set our sights too high.'

'Oh, stop it, Mother,' cried Julia. 'You are depressing, as depressing as Edith!'

Julia was glad to be home, glad to kick off her tight, pinching, high-heeled shoes, happy to get out of her dress and put on the lovely soft housecoat that her mother had made for her, and as happy as a kitten to be sitting at a corner of the table in front of a bowl of steaming hot chocolate. After all, she was only just eighteen.

As Julia had guessed, Edith was indeed passing through a difficult phase. Not that there was any one thing in particular that you could put your finger on. At the store, Edith's prestige was increasing. Her buyer not only constantly sought her advice but when they were together the conversation occasionally strayed from purely business considerations to the human and personal element. The two women worked so quickly and smoothly together that it was bound to come to this. The 'octopus', as Edith called her, was looking fondly forward to having a first child and suddenly Edith, looking at her superior, saw in her not a softening enemy but a youthful and extremely captivating woman. The tiniest incident happened, for instance, to confirm this view. The telephone rang and the 'octopus', whose arms were full of new autumn models, turned to Edith and said: 'Be a dear and answer that!' Lifting the receiver she said politely, in case it was somebody very senior in the management: 'Good morning. This is Edith in the dress department.'

'Hello, Edith!' came a warm, masculine voice. 'How nice to hear you. Good morning. Is my wife with you?'

'Of course,' said Edith, handing the telephone to her buyer. 'Madam, it is your husband.'

Edith caught herself feeling warm and happy. He had called her by her name as if they were old friends. This could only mean that the octopus had talked about her so constantly at home that to the husband she was a real, live person. Well, it might be a very small thing but it was a nice, human thing to happen, and it meant that Edith was gradually carving a place out for herself not only in the store but as a Londoner in London. When the buyer put the receiver down, she said to Edith:

'My husband has been to the funeral of one of the directors of his company, and the chairman has just told him that he is being nominated to his seat on the board. He will be the youngest—the baby amongst the directors. Isn't that wonderful!'

Edith smiled, reflecting that it had needed the death of this unknown director to bring sudden happiness, new vistas of success to Helen. Conversely it showed that Helen was, in fact, standing excitedly on tiptoe on the threshold of everything, a young husband's future career and her first baby! It struck her bitterly that her own father's death must have brought advancement to nobody!

This, of course, brought her back to Archie. This was the sombre part. Laura was more than ever affectionate. In many ways Laura had been Edith's ideal of what a young woman should be—beautiful, tender, intelligent, the gayest mother of two sweet little girls. The events of the last few weeks had robbed her, only temporarily one hoped, of her extreme freshness, but it was the elder girl, Clarissa, whom Edith felt most sorry for—the girl who dreamt of being a dancer and on whose table there were innumerable photographs of ballet stars. She had even taken to telephoning to Edith, like a real little grown-up woman, to recount the worries of her school life and her total incomprehension of what had come over her father with whom, like all young girls, she was a little in love.

All this in turn merely stressed the point that Archie was remaining somewhat aloof just now. Not that Edith perceived in his behaviour any less tenderness or affection. It was simply that he was fully occupied by the examinations which, if he passed them successfully, as she felt sure he would, must surely allow him to step into a place of senior importance in his father's firm. Meanwhile he did neglect her. There was no doubt about that. At one period she had trembled every time she found herself alone with him for fear that he would ask without warning some embarrassing question about her family or her past. Now he too seldom put her in that position. They had drifted into a long moment of waiting, of expectation—a hiatus.

'Congratulate me!' cried Archie joyfully on the telephone. 'I have got through all my examinations.'

Alone in the flat, with the prospect of a long, dateless evening stretching ahead of her, Edith had done what she invariably did on such occasions, put her head under the shower to start the complicated ritual of washing and setting her hair. Just as she was pouring the shampoo on, the telephone in the living-room had rung. 'Drat it!' she thought. 'It's probably not even for me!' So she let it ring.

When, after a few minutes, it started up again, she had rinsed the shampoo out of her hair. Accordingly she wound a towel round her head and skipped barefoot into the living-room. Archie's voice sent a tremor down her spine. But she was careful to control her excitement.

'I expect you are glad,' she said testily. 'About the examinations, I mean. They got you down, didn't they? Did you do well?'

'I just scraped through,' he said.

This was a flagrant understatement. He had done brilliantly as, at heart, she guessed he would. He was that type of boy.

'Are you alone?' he asked.

'Of course I am alone. Otherwise I would not have been obliged to come to the telephone half naked and with dripping hair. I shall catch my death of cold.'

'Let me come round, all the same. I won't say a word about the state of your hair. I don't even mind if you are naked. Besides, I bet you look stunning with a Turkish towel round your top. Laura is always ravishing when she emerges from the bathroom like that! I shall jump into the car and I'll be with you in twenty minutes. O.K.?'

'Certainly not. I look terrible.'

'You women are all the same. Clarissa has stolen Laura's

manicure set and is polishing her nails. Laura tells her she will get the sack from school but she says she doesn't care. She also says: "Tell Edith I love her!"'

Edith laughed.

'It's a trick to soften me up!' she said. 'And I am still catching my death of cold!'

'Then that is that. Put the pins in your hair. That is what girls generally do, isn't it? And put on the kettle, I will be round in twenty minutes.'

Edith pinned up her hair, tidied the flat, plugged in the electric kettle and switched on the drier. While she held it over her head, she examined the dresses in her wardrobe, wondering what to put on. Twenty minutes gave her very little time.

The unexpected phone call put a slightly different complexion on Archie's recent behaviour. Laura may well have been right in suggesting that her brother's examinations were chiefly responsible for his silences and apparent neglect. A great deal, perhaps nothing less than his future, had possibly been at stake. Under present-day conditions Archie's father would not want to bring him into a senior position without outstanding qualifications. Inherited wealth and prestige needed to be backed by academic competence.

She had, of course, gone over all this before. The crisis in Laura's marriage had at least as much to do with Archie's silences as worry about his examinations. What sort of a man was their father? Still young, from what Edith could gather, still very much the dynamic chairman of his go-ahead firm. Not a man to trifle with, she supposed. On two or three occasions during the last month he had come specially to London to see Laura. But he had also come to see his son-in-law, believing that this situation, so grave in its possible consequences, could perhaps be more easily settled between men than in an atmosphere of loose talk, violence and hasty recrimination. Calmly, over a conference table, in muted, polite voices, men settled grave industrial disputes. In the same way, therefore, Archie's and Laura's father wanted to understand, however difficult it might be, his son-in-law's criminal, inexplicable behaviour. Men did not take catastrophic action without reason. Laura had said: 'Father is taking him out to dinner.' To his club perhaps. They would drink claret and port.

'If your father forgives him,' Edith had asked Laura, 'will you?'

'A woman always forgives,' said Laura.

Her father did not, in fact, achieve the desired reconciliation. His son-in-law proved resolutely stubborn; he claimed that he was passionately in love for the first time and he was prepared to accept all the consequences. This was one of the rare occasions on which Laura's father was unable to make use of a cheque book. One could not even be certain that patience would help. Fundamentally, Arthur was a good man with about the same number of qualities and defects that go to make up most husbands. One could even say that at the time of his marriage to Laura he had sincerely loved her, and that for several years, until well after the birth of the two girls, the marriage appeared to possess all the elements of success. It is only when a man is suddenly swept off his feet by an uncontrollable passion for another woman that reason ceases to have any effect. He put forward no excuses, willingly accepted all the blame and would, of course, forgo custody of the children. For Laura's and Archie's father this drama had come as a severe blow. During a life of struggle, he had steeled himself against quite different forms of ill wind, against the fear of business recessions, of prolonged labour disputes, of social strife, of the illness of his wife or his children and of Archie not turning out to be the son he had hoped and prayed for. None of these things had so far happened. Success had crowned his energy and determination and his honesty in business. The wind that now struck him by this damaging action against his daughter Laura was as mean as it was unexpected.

Ensconced on the sofa in the girls' living-room, his long legs crossed, Archie watched Edith slowly and methodically applying mascara while she was intently listening to him. He said: 'I hate to see Father so nonplussed, even temporarily. He has never been exactly tender with us at the best of times, and neither of us has blamed him for this, it was all part of his natural rectitude, but now he will probably want to put us through a period of blood and sweat to get the family on an even keel again. Take me, for instance. I rather looked forward to spending another year in London. Now, Father wants me to join him in our main offices in the Midlands. He talks of setting Laura up again so that she can make a new start. I think the house in Regent's Park is in Arthur's name, not in hers. That tends to complicate things. Arthur is not particularly good at making money, and I would not be surprised if he has overspent himself trying to run two households. As for Laura, she has never known what it is for a young woman not to have charge accounts at the best dress houses.' He laughed. 'I don't blame her, do you?'

Edith appeared very intent on the business of completing her make-up, but in fact her mind was only half on it. She was like a chess player pondering over an important move. She said into the mirror:

'I really don't see, Archie, that things have changed so much for you. It's surely immaterial whether you should remain in London a little longer or not. As you have taken an honours degree at Oxford and passed all your subsequent examinations, whatever they are, your future in the firm is assured. And even if the firm were to be taken over by a still larger, still more important one, you are of the right age to be taken over with it. Your father will find you a wealthy wife and you will have the good sense to see that she behaves herself. More and more I see you resembling your father, working hard and sticking to the straight and narrow. Growing just a tiny bit stouter and exchanging your car for another. So don't ask me to shed any tears for you, Archie!'

She was glad that Archie had done well in his examinations, pleased that he had thought it worth while to come round to tell her about it, but suddenly tired of the family's lamentations. It struck her that she was seriously running the risk of wasting another evening. Clearly the father, whether according to plan or accidentally, was astutely moving to place himself between Archie and herself. She would not have been surprised to hear a voice crying gruffly: Check! She would have a good cry later, but at this juncture tears were unthinkable.

Though she did not know it, Archie was looking at her intently:

'Why on earth are you telling me all this? Why are you suddenly so unnaturally aggressive? Don't you know that I love you! I have never ceased to love you from that very first morning when I caught sight of you standing miserably on the kerb waiting for a taxi to take you to the dentist's. I loved everything about you, your lovely dark hair, your deep, mysterious eyes, your beautiful breasts and shapely legs. When Laura and I invited you into the car I knew that you were the one girl in the world I wanted to marry.'

Edith stared into space. The tall-ceilinged room of this Victorian house seemed to be crashing down all about her. She must not move. She must not breathe. She must try desperately to understand.

'Laura's unhappiness shook me,' Archie was saying, 'but all through it I felt the warmth and comfort of your presence. If I were completely honest I would say that I was always alternating between grief for her and joy with you. The end of her marriage, if it proves to be that, only heightened the excitement I felt to have discovered a girl I knew instinctively I could no longer do without.'

Now all Edith's care with her make-up went for naught. Tears exploded, streaming down her cheeks. She wept with love, with bitterness, with frustration, and with the knowledge that what had to be said must now be said, that this declaration of love so eagerly, so passionately awaited marked the ineluctable end of it, as the butterfly's glory announces its death.

Archie went on saying what lovers say, and Edith's tears were for him merely the tears of a happy girl. Edith wanted desperately to prolong this happiness like the tune of a popular love song heard on the evening air. If it were her destiny to hear nothing else but this, then it must last her till the end of her days. She would at least have heard the words that every girl dreams of hearing once.

Archie suddenly glanced at his watch and said:

'Let us go somewhere in the car and celebrate!' His hands met hers. His fingers caressed the place where he would slip the engagement ring. He said: 'I am incorrigible. I have done all the talking, and there is so much I want to know about you.'

'My hair is not dry,' she said, 'and I look a wreck. I can't come out and there is something I have got to tell you. I love you desperately, Archie, and I was terrified I would never hear you tell me that you loved me. There may have been moments when I felt it, but feeling it is not the same as being told it. I shall never love anybody as I have loved you, but there was once somebody else in my home town, a boy who promised to marry me and then abandoned me when I became pregnant. I ran in a panic to a charlatan he knew about. There was a miscarriage, a scandal and my family told me I would not be welcome back. I have never seen my mother since. My father died a short time ago, and for all I know I may have been partly responsible for his death. My aunt whom I met by accident on the steamer on my way to Ostend this summer is the only member of my family to have forgiven me so far. I know that my mother, who is living alone, must be unhappy, and I have a younger sister who is just married, according to my aunt.

'After the miscarriage I fainted in a railway station and woke up in a hospital where I nearly died. My mother took one look at me and walked out. Almost anything that can happen to a stupid, naïve girl had happened to me, and I do not even know if I can have children, though that, I tell myself cynically, is in my state of unhappiness immaterial.

'I learnt to hate men, and I never thought I could love anybody again until I met you. If you had asked me to sleep with you, I would have hated you and sent you packing. As it is you made me love you. Not that my present state is any better. Because now that you have made me love you, I am going to make you hate me. You see, Archie, I was doomed no matter which way I turned. I was doomed except for this one thing you have given me and which you can never take away, this momentary illusion of being loved and of being able to almost grasp happiness. But I am so terribly sad, Archie, to have spoilt your first love. For I am your first love, aren't I? I did my utmost from the beginning to prevent you from falling for me. I left you hanging about hotel foyers and never answered your phone calls. Occasionally I even lied to you. Leave me, Archie! Don't try to sympathize. You will merely make things worse than they are. I ought to have told Laura and made Laura help me, but Laura suddenly turned from being strong to being weak, and when I discovered that she needed my help, I did not dare ask for hers. In any case I doubt if she would have listened very attentively to my misfortunes. The shock of her own has been too great. So please, Archie, go and try to forget me, and whatever you do, drive carefully. Don't take it out on the car. Too many people need you—your father, Laura, your little nieces!'

She pushed him gently to the door. He made no resistance. He looked miserable to the point of being stunned. Once again as so many times before in a crisis, she was proving her strength. Her arm encircled his waist, pushing, anxious to end this intolerable moment and yet secretly she was longing to lay her head against his chest and sob.

She waited for him to run down to his car, knowing that once he had gone he would not come back. She heard the car door slam, the engine being revved up, the car going off down the road. The scene that had been haunting her for weeks with its inevitable outcome was at last over. She would never see him again. Clarissa would not be allowed to telephone. Laura would cease to ask for her sympathy and advice. They would build a wall of silence between her and themselves. The future little dress buyer, the confident little career girl, was like a sparrow with both legs broken.

6

THE next morning when Julia went to her locker she found a piece of paper with the words: 'Come up and see me if you can. Edith.'

She screwed it up, threw it into a corner and went to the mirror to start drawing the contour of her lips, but she noticed that her hand was shaking. Her mother may well have been right. She was overtired, but mentally rather than physically. Time had begun to drag. Nothing was happening and she was eighteen. Francis had given no further sign of life, and it was clear that she had failed to make any strong impression on him. There was no question about it, she was a naïve little goose, and so far had no experience at all of the other sex. Was it that she had no sex-appeal, that she was stupid (from a man's point of view) or altogether too much mother's little girl? She moved exclusively in a woman's world—her mother's, her mother's clients, the store and the girls who worked in it.

'Let us see,' she whispered to her reflection as she filled in the drawn lines with orange lipstick. 'Women do not encourage other women. They dissect them. Miss Pauline considers me just plain dumb, saying that youth does not last. Had not some Elizabethan poet said the same thing?' The client from Maddox Street? Well, Julia could hardly be expected to tear a leaf out of her book! Daisy had started with a flourish, but just look where it had landed her! As for Iris, she was not the sort of girl another girl would particularly want to copy! Betty was like a filly who always came in last in a race. She also did not inspire confidence.

When Julia arrived at her department Betty was reading her horoscope in the morning paper. It was, she said, looking up and saying good morning, unusually good, but though it was good in the morning it was to prove better still in the evening. Her face was bright with hope. 'What do you suppose is going to happen to me?' she exclaimed, rather too loudly for the correct behaviour of a department chief in the presence of her assistant. She laughed. 'Well, it did not start well at home,' she said. 'Mother burnt the milk at breakfast and Dad upset the tea on the clean cloth.'

The girls worked swiftly to get everything ready for the first customers, and then Julia, taking advantage of her companion's good humour, asked for permission to run up a moment to see Edith on the first floor. 'Of course,' said Betty, 'but take care that Mrs Davies doesn't catch you. Or, if she does, find a good excuse.'

Julia sped to the service lift where the old man with his osier basket was about to press the 'up' button. 'Wait!' cried Julia. 'Where are you going to?'

'To the restaurant floor,' he answered, 'but there is room for you to squeeze in, and if you want to stop off at the first, that is all right. I shall be glad of the company!' As they went up he said: 'Next month I have to retire. They won't let me stay any longer, so you won't be seeing me around any more. I shall go to my son's place and cultivate his garden.'

'Then,' said Julia, depositing a light kiss on his wrinkled forehead, 'I wish you luck. You were kind to me on the first day I came here.'

Julia found Edith pale and drawn. 'What on earth is the matter with you?' she cried. 'Are you ill?' Edith was brushing face powder off the collar of a navy blue dress that had been left there by a customer. Looking up into Julia's anxious face, her dark eyes filled with tears.

'Oh, Julia,' she cried. 'It is finished. I told Archie everything last night and now it is all over.'

She sobbed unrestrainedly and then asked:

'Julia, do you think your mother would let me come and sleep at your place tonight? I can't face going back to the flat where it all happened. I would see him everywhere.'

She was waiting desperately for the answer.

'I have brought a few things with me—enough for the night, I mean. I can't stand the idea of being alone, and I don't dare go to my aunt's flat. Aunt is not the sort of woman to sympathize with a girl who has failed. She likes me when I am sure of myself and successful. So you see, Julia, you have become my only friend. I have nobody else I can turn to.'

When Julia brought Edith home that evening they found Julia's mother on the floor kneeling in front of the contents of large cardboard box. She was very gay and explained that she had suddenly acquired a new source of income. The box was full of dresses, skirts, blouses, that needed small modifications or repairs, and every garment had a piece of paper pinned to it setting out the details of what was to be done. 'See!' exclaimed Julia's mother. 'The hem of this skirt needs shortening by a couple of inches. This dress wants lengthening. The sleeves of this other one must be cut off, and here is a skirt that needs a new hook on the petersham. All without the fuss of a single fitting! Isn't it wonderful?'

'How did it happen?' asked Julia, delving into the box, and examining various things that her mother had not yet taken out.

'It happened thanks to you,' said her mother. 'I took your beige coat to the cleaner the other day, and while I was waiting my turn a young customer was bewailing the fact that she had wanted to shorten her red skirt but that she had never been taught to sew. She looked so young and helpless and I thought she probably had a baby at home and could not be expected to know everything, so I said to her: "Let me shorten your skirt for you. I have a daughter not much younger than you are, and I would like to feel that if ever she needed it, a stranger would give her a helping hand. I will take your skirt home and do what needs doing, and in less than an hour I will bring it back to the young lady behind the counter so that it can go out to be cleaned." I shortened the skirt and brought it back to the cleaner. The

229

girl behind the counter said: "If you could do odd jobs for us like that, we would give you more than a dozen such garments every day and you could make a little fortune. We pay very well." So here I am, girls, on my way to making a fortune. Don't mix things up, Julia. Imagine what would happen if I cut the sleeves off the wrong dress!'

'It's a splendid idea!' cried Edith, carried away by the thought of starting a profitable business. 'See that your customers are aware of all this new work. If they think you are frantically busy, they will prove themselves infinitely more generous.'

'By the way,' said Julia. 'Edith would like to spend a few nights with us. She can share my room. You don't mind, do you?'

'I'll be delighted,' cried her mother. 'She may stay with us as long as she likes.'

'She has a problem in connection with her flat,' said Julia, thinking that an explanation was necessary.

'Naturally,' said her mother, 'there are bound to be problems with shared flats. I expect she left the bath tap running while she talked to Archie on the phone.'

'That's about it,' said Edith, 'only I more or less drowned!'

Julia's mother put the box away and prepared supper. She was never taken by surprise on these occasions. The girls would have a lovely hot meal and she would get everything ready while they went to Julia's room to put themselves at their ease.

After supper she told their fortunes and, rather to her surprise, the knave of hearts came strongly in Edith's cards. Although Edith pretended not to attach any importance to it, her eyes lost their redness and she looked almost happy. All three went early to bed. They were tired with the tiredness of carrying about with them problems that, with variations, were common to all three, those of being temporarily—but not, they felt certain, for always—without the love of a man.

In the morning the two girls walked through the streets of Soho to work. Edith had recovered much of that quiet determination which marked her character. She would prove to the world that success lay within herself. Just before mid-day she was called to the telephone. Her heart beat furiously. Alas, it was only her aunt. 'Come and see me after work,' said her aunt. 'Take a cab. I will pay for it.'

Giving the news to Julia during the lunch hour, Edith said: 'Tell your mother I will be home just as soon as I can but not to wait supper for me. Aunt is sure to give me something to eat. Tell her also that I think she is the sweetest person in the whole world. You have no idea how much good she does me.'

'There is so little she or I can do,' said Julia. 'But last night Mother guessed right away. She told me so this morning. She even said that if ever we can afford to take a place of our own, rather larger, she wants you to come and share it with us.'

When Edith arrived at her aunt's house, she found her arranging autumn flowers in a tall cut-glass vase. She was dressed with her usual elegance, her hair beautifully done. As Edith crossed the room to meet her, the older woman smiled affectionately, complimented her on her appearance, and said:

'I hope, Edith dear, you did not have a more important engagement. I want to talk to you about your mother. She keeps writing to me, not about you, so have no fear, I am far too conscious of the pleasure of our relationship to betray the slightest confidence. I am proud to have you as a niece! No, your mother writes about your sister, who has decided that she and her husband would save a great deal of money by going to live with her. Your sister thinks that now your mother is a widow, and that you show no sign of returning home, the house is too big for her. It is none of my business, and I am not sure to what extent it is any of yours, but all the same I feel you ought to know. The house probably is too large for your mother alone, and it would be better for her to have people at hand if she were to be ill. On the other hand, your mother resents your sister's rowdy friends. She claims that her son-in-law brings crowds of young people back and they play raucous music till past midnight, drink her whisky, grind out their cigarettes on her carpet, eat her food and make her feel that she is no longer in her own home. It is her misfortune always to have made a mess of her life. She has excellent principles but is apt to apply them wrongly. Your father, like so many of his kind, was a weak, ineffectual man who would have needed a much more competent, strong-willed wife.'

Edith thought the flowers, Michaelmas daisies, sad. She was not interested in what her aunt was saying.

'Perhaps,' continued her aunt, 'your mother is being made to suffer a little of what she made you suffer. This would be a sad retribution because, though she was wrong, she probably meant well. Don't you feel that you should fly to her help?'

'Both Mother and my sister have done without me for so long,' said Edith, 'that they taught me how to do without them. This may not be Christian charity, but I think that even you would not advise me to go back to the Midlands at this stage.'

'If ever you were to marry,' said the aunt, looking very slyly at her niece, 'you would doubtless have to tell her.'

She waited for the reaction, hoping that by this means she might discover for herself how things were going between Edith and the young man of whose family and high prospects she fully approved.

'My chances of making a good marriage,' said Edith, turning away, 'are practically nil, my chances of making a bad one almost unlimited. As I have set my mind against the latter, I shall continue to carve a future out for myself in the store. After all, marriage is not everything for a girl!'

She bent down, buried her face in her hands and sobbed convulsively. Her aunt had now the answer she had sought and feared. She looked thoughtfully at her niece, full of pity but not surprised. She was not the woman to make a useless show of sympathy. She knew what her beautiful niece was up against and reflected that there must be better ways than tears to set her forth again on a strong, determined path.

She took from the second finger of her right hand a ring of five flawless rubies set in gold, a Victorian piece her husband had once given her at her own request after he had brought off a particularly successful business deal. Rubies of such a deep colour were becoming rare but, more important still, they were the stone of perfect love. She was a rich woman now. Her hopes of love were replaced by her banking account. She would give to this girl, her niece, something she hoped would bring her all the true love in the world. Making room for herself beside Edith on the armchair, Edith's favourite armchair, she took her niece's right hand in hers and slipped the ring on the second finger.

'May your true love run smooth!' she said, kissing her on the forehead. 'And come to lunch on Sunday!'

The next morning Edith told Julia's mother that she would go back to her own flat for the weekend. This seemed to her the right decision. She was no longer willing to shelter from what might prove humiliating or remindful of her defeat. The ring her aunt had slipped on her finger gave her the same sort of quiet assurance as a dress signed by a great *couture* house. It put on her its seal of unquestioned authority.

She needed to be once again amongst her own possessions, her own bed, her wardrobe with her clothes hanging in the right places, her shoes ranged along the bottom. Little by little, too, a desire to watch over her interests had come over her. The flat was in her name. She was responsible for it, and she must be sure that the other girls had not left the bath taps running, the gas turned on, a hot iron on the living-room carpet to singe it or to set the place on fire. But most of all she wanted to be back just in case somebody had rung up or left a message—Archie first and foremost. Yes, she still dared to hope. Or Laura, or Clarissa. One could never tell. Her rubies might be working their unlikely possibility.

Julia's mother politely but not too quickly acquiesced. Though she had admittedly a rather special affection for Edith, who was to be pitied, she was anxious to recover sole possession of both her flat and her daughter before the weekend. Besides, she had a curious habit when her nerves began to trouble her: she embarked on a thorough spring cleaning which, of course, could take place as easily in autumn as at any other time of the year. Her 'spring cleaning' was as symptomatic of her nerves as Julia's furniture moving was of her periods. Obviously it was better to have guests out of the way before such an operation began.

She bade farewell to Edith from her accustomed place at the living-room window, and watched the two girls go off to work together. She then took a shopping basket from a hook in the kitchen and set off for her usual Saturday expedition into Soho. When she reached Daisy's home, she hesitated. Daisy's mother had recovered from her pneumonia and was now up and about. It might be worth while for Julia's mother to invite Daisy's mother to come shopping with her. Standing squarely in front of the door, she gave two taps with the knocker.

Daisy's mother, having opened the front door suspiciously, stood in front of her friend surprised and somewhat out of breath because everything was an effort just now. Daisy's mother hated raps on the front door. She never knew what they might portend. If her husband happened to be at home he would hear them and there would be the usual explaining to do. When the girls were at fault, for instance, she always tried to take the blame. Her husband was a Yorkshireman and could be very stubborn and infinitely difficult. Before coming south to work as a porter at Covent Garden market he had been a docker. He was strong physically, mentally autocratic and occasionally hot-tempered. She herself was from Blackburn in Lancashire and often yearned for the soft talk and extreme good neighbourliness of her home county. Their son had died when he was only five. Since then her husband had tended to treat his two daughters in an aggressive, dictatorial way as if to make them feel the inadequacy of being girls.

Though Daisy's mother had recovered from her illness, she still puffed and had moments of giddiness. She should, of course, have taken time off to recuperate properly in a convalescent home under the control of the hospital, but though this stout, almost waddling, woman was just a grain of sand in the ocean of humanity, she was a veritable bulwark to her family. None of them could have existed without her. Actually Daisy had never even set off for the Channel Islands. In spite of all her angry words she had come back next day without even mentioning her fury about the £5 notes (there were eight of them in all!) discovered between the sheets. She had found a job with a diamond merchant in Hatton Garden.

Having found a shopping basket of her own, as she accompanied her friend slowly down the street in the direction of Cambridge Circus, Daisy's mother said:

'Daisy is engaged!'

'What?' cried Julia's mother, outraged.

'Yes,' said Daisy's mother. 'To a boy from Warrington in my home county.'

The news stunned Julia's mother, who thought that of all the unfair things, nothing could be more unfair than for Daisy to have virtually found herself a husband while Julia was still without anybody more serious than Francis, who was obviously not going to propose. Even if Julia had wanted him.

But already Daisy's mother had reverted to the subject of her health.

'My illness has left me so weak,' she said, 'that I can scarcely lift the sheets to put them in the copper.' She shot a sideways glance at Julia's mother, and added in a rather pitiful voice: 'I'm only forty-six. I shouldn't feel worn out yet, should I?'

'Of course not,' said Julia's mother. 'As it happens, I intended to spring clean my own place today, but as soon as I am through I will come and give you a hand. Would you like that? After all, it would be only a small thing between neighbours.'

'Thank you,' said Daisy's mother. 'I would like that!'

Julia's mother decided that she would not tell her daughter about Daisy's engagement. Daisy was greedy. She wanted everything. Some girls were like that. The worst catastrophe hardly affected them. They bent their heads momentarily, but as soon as it was over they looked brazenly up again into the sun! Whereas she and Julia were by nature too gentle-womanly and docile. A feather would knock them over.

When Edith had turned her key in the front door and hurried through the small hall into the living-room, she could sense right away that nobody was home. The feeling of emptiness and finality must not be allowed to gain ascendancy ever again. She would have a long, hot bath. As she undressed and went naked into the bathroom she looked for the hundredth time that day at the ring with the five blood-red rubies. She would never take it off, not for a single moment. Girls sometimes took off their rings or their bracelets to wash their hands or to make up and left them in public lavatories. Her mother had warned her never to do that. Now that she was going to run her own life, be her own mistress, she might even have the ring insured. Not that money could ever replace it, but this flat and its contents were insured and perhaps the ring could be added to the policy. A career girl must learn to do certain things to protect herself, things that a husband would normally do for his wife.

It was nearly seven on Sunday evening and she had half expected one of the girls to be back. All three were away for the weekend. One had gone to Edinburgh to see her parents, the other to Bradford, the third had gone with her Harley Street specialist friend to a country club on the south coast. Edith was beginning to appreciate less the curious quality of these weekends that separated friends who lived under the same roof. Her companions might come back late this evening, they might not come back till early Monday morning. They might even go straight to work. Edith's friendship with Julia had not accustomed her to loneliness.

This Sunday had been very special, however. Edith, as arranged, had gone to lunch with her aunt, and there she found to her immense pleasure that her Uncle Esmond had come back from his business trip. Uncle Esmond, like his wife, had taken her under his wing. It was as if both of them had discovered a new youthfulness in the presence of their niece.

After lunch, because it was one of those radiant afternoons of this Indian summer, when the leaves were beginning to turn to all sorts of reds and browns, and the air smelt cool and fresh, Uncle Esmond had driven them both to Hampton Court in his new car. In late summer he took them to Rottingdean; in autumn he liked to have tea at an excellent hotel opposite the palace gates so that they could dream of Henry the Eighth, Cardinal Wolsey and all the glory past and present of the swift-running Thames. Uncle Esmond liked to talk history and motor cars to his eager young niece, who was so attentive to everything he said. She was gentle and polite to him, and she was proving in every way a late but delightful compensation for their lack of children. Her presence, he noted with satisfaction, had also greatly softened the character of his wife, so that his happiness was twofold. In these circumstances his home had become quite a different place to come back to, warmer and more welcoming. The two women so often revealed traits that amused him. They liked when they came to Hampton Court to feed the swans on the river and the deer in the park, bringing a loaf of bread especially for them, and he would stand a few paces away on the towing path or in the bracken and watch them doing so, thinking how refreshing and resting it was for a man to see two women, an older one and a younger one, so amicably, eagerly, talking together.

They had driven Edith back to her flat. Uncle Esmond, with old-fashioned courtesy, had jumped out to open the car door for her, and to walk with her the few yards that separated them from the pillared steps leading up to the Victorian house. He always did this as if he were afraid that on winter nights she might get lost in the fog or on summer nights she might be kidnapped! Although Edith was amused she liked him all the more for it. She was never a girl to be afraid of what other people might think or say. Was it not her uncle who had given the ruby ring to her aunt, and been so touchingly pleased when her aunt had given it to her? She kissed him playfully on the tip of his nose, and blew a kiss to her aunt, who had remained in the car. Then she ran up the steps and slipped her key in the lock.

She emerged refreshed from her bath. Her aunt had been sent some new orange nail varnish from New York. Edith had admired it at lunch and her aunt, with her usual generosity, had given her the rest of the bottle, slipping it into her niece's handbag. This was the time to give herself a manicure and try it. In future she must take even greater care of her hands so that they formed an elegant, worthy setting for her ruby ring!

Before leaving the bathroom she filled the washbasin with warm water and soap suds to wash the underclothes she had removed. The bathroom was filled with steam and she began singing a tune that the girls hummed at the store. Her thin but agreeable voice, accompanied by the humming of the geyser, spurred her forward. 'But I do not sing because I am happy!' she caught herself thinking. 'I sing because I am alone in this empty flat and because I have a whole, long, terrible evening stretching ahead of me!' Presently the words of the love song died on her lips and she felt a tickling first in her nose, and then in her throat, that she recognized as the precursor of tears. As she squeezed the water out of the limp, formless bra, her tears began to fall on to it.

When she had rinsed everything out in clear water she hung it all on the line which she and the other girls had fixed above the bath. Like bright flowers in a garden after rain, the silk dripped into the bottom of the empty bath. Feeling energetic in clean, freshly ironed underclothes, she decided to pass the carpet sweeper over the floor of the living-room. After that she would choose a becoming dress and read a novel. The noise of the sweeper, like the hissing of the geyser, steadied her nerves.

238

She paused in front of the tall living-room windows to look out into the broad avenue below. People were already coming back from weekends in the country. Taxis drew up and she could hear voices and the drivers jerking up the flags of their clocks.

She was putting the sweeper back into the cupboard of the hall when there was a ring at the front door. 'There's Claudia!' she cried happily. 'I shall not be alone after all.' Probably Claudia had mislaid her door key at the bottom of her large handbag as she often did. Having heard the noise of the sweeper she had rung rather than start searching for it.

'Coming!' cried Edith, pushing the sweeper into the cupboard and opening the front door. It was Archie! 'Oh!' she cried. She was in a pink crêpe de chine slip, and in her confusion the blood ran to the roots of her hair. She remained motionless and tongue-tied.

'Can I come in?' he asked.

She nodded and stepped back to let him in.   -

'Give me time to put a dress on,' she said. 'You know the way, don't you?'

She went into her bedroom and stood for a moment trying to steady her nerves. 'I must keep calm,' she murmured and started to dab eau de Cologne over her forehead and along the inside of her arms. She put on a favourite dress, changed her shoes and arranged her hair. Fortunately she had thought of doing her hands, and the new nail enamel looked nice.

Feeling rather more sure of herself, she joined him in the living-room and asked for news of Laura and the little girls.

'They are well,' said Archie, 'but they miss you.'

'I miss them too,' she said.

Archie looked at her for a long moment and then said:

'I saw you come back this evening, rather more than an hour ago, with an old gentleman on the tip of whose nose you deposited a dutiful kiss. Was he a member of your family?'

'He is my Uncle Esmond,' she said. 'He and Aunt took me to Hampton Court this afternoon. But what were you doing here rather more than an hour ago? Were you by any chance spying on me? And if so, why did you not come in earlier?'

'I was nervous,' he said.

'Of me?'

'Perhaps. What have you been doing this last week? I kept on telephoning. The girls said you were sleeping out.'

'I went to Julia's place,' she said. 'Let us say that I needed a change of scene. Julia's mother was very good to me. But now, as you can see for yourself, I am back and I was cleaning the place up a bit.'

'I have been very unhappy,' said Archie.

'I have not exactly been happy myself,' said Edith.

They stood facing each other, awkwardly fencing. He took a step forward and seized her hands in his. Suddenly his eyes fell on the ruby ring and he exclaimed:

'Who dared give you this? I should be the only one to give you rubies!'

'Somebody else had the same idea!' she said, smiling.

His face fell. Momentarily he wondered if there really was somebody else, but the fact that she wore the ring on her right hand reassured him. The Victorian gold setting marked it out also as a family piece. Nevertheless he asked hesitatingly:

'Tell me, Edith! Swear it! There isn't anybody else?'

'No,' she said. 'There isn't anybody else, and I don't suppose there ever will be. My aunt gave me these rubies because I was unhappy. Uncle Esmond had given them to her to bring her luck, and she wanted to pass her good fortune on to me. It was sweet of her, don't you think? Do you believe in that sort of thing?'

'Edith, I love you! I came here this evening to tell you so. When I saw you come back with your uncle, I wanted you more than I have ever done, but I was nervous. I was nervous because when we were together the other evening, I should not have allowed you to push me out. I lacked the strength of my own convictions. I was not strong at the precise moment when I should have been. A man should not allow himself to be pushed around by a girl. This evening when I saw you saying goodbye to your uncle, I was afraid you would think that I had not measured up to being worth marrying. I jumped back into the car and drove twice round the parks. That gave me the courage I needed. I came right back—and here I am. I thought maybe that if you agreed to be my wife we could get married quietly. Smart weddings don't always bring corresponding happiness. Consider Laura's, for instance. It was a real society wedding with hundreds of guests. The whole lot. Alas, it did not turn out so well, did it?'

He took her gently in his arms and added:

'A quiet wedding, in a country church. I know a village in the Lake District. Would you agree to that, Edith?'

They went out to supper to celebrate, and when Edith came back it was past midnight. None of the girls was yet back but the apartment was now full of joy, and Edith thought: 'How can I wait to tell Julia? Why has she not got a telephone?'

7

RAIN was falling lightly, as it had fallen on that first morning when Julia had set out in such trepidation to start work at the store. The streets were wet and muddy. She no longer needed to economize so much on her stockings but, she told herself, it was definitely not the sort of day to drop a glove or a scarf!

As she approached the tailor's shop owned by the Bishops, she saw that it was closed and that there was an upright black board nailed to the front. Who in the family had died? Presumably the father or the mother of the two boys? Strange, she thought, that we were not told about it, and a slight feeling of guilt came over her as she became aware of her almost total indifference in the matter. She wondered whether to knock and make polite enquiries; but fearing to be late for work she decided to come back this way during the lunch hour. She and her mother had had a slight altercation at breakfast. Julia was wearing the new dress Edith had put aside for her in the sale and her mother, who had mildly approved of it when Julia brought it home, now declared that it was far too short. To which Julia answered with a touch of humour that it was no shorter than those of other girls of her age, and that if her mother really thought it was too short, she was not in tune with the younger generation. Mother had pinched her lips, on which she seldom put even the faintest suspicion of lipstick, and had murmured: 'Well, I never thought I would live to hear my daughter speak to me like that!'

The terrible thing was that Julia had not kissed her mother goodbye when she left home.

Mrs Davies came to the department soon after the store

had opened and said in Betty's presence: 'Julia, dear, if Betty has no objection, I would rather like you to come down to the store-room with me.'

'Of course, Madam,' said Betty, not quite certain to which of them, to Julia or to herself, a compliment was meant. But Julia knew because Mrs Davies had smiled at her in a protective, affectionate way.

The store-room contained a vast assortment of cases, boxes and goods. This treasure cave was under the charge of a certain Mrs Topper who had short curly grey hair and a club foot.

She had come originally to the store as a cleaner and had moved up through the various grades by dint of an infinite capacity for making herself useful to every single member of the staff who came her way. Her authority, which by now was unassailable, acted to some extent as compensation for her infirmity. Quite apart from this, she had a cockney's innate good sense which often told her, more accurately than her superiors, which line would sell and which would not.

The three women—Mrs Topper, Mrs Davies and Julia— worked swiftly; and Mrs Topper saw to it, as she always did in such circumstances, that hot coffee and cream and a plate of sweet biscuits were sent down at eleven on a prettily arranged tray from the restaurant. Mrs Topper thought of everything—and she was all the more particular about the appetizing quality of her 'elevenses' because nobody, not even a senior buyer, was allowed to smoke on account of the billowing reams of tissue paper and the many inflammable goods in the room.

Mrs Topper said: 'There is a great improvement lately in your department, Mrs Davies. The management is most aware of it.'

'I think they are,' said Mrs Davies, blushing slightly at the compliment. 'In all fairness I should point out that I am particularly fortunate in my two girls.'

On the way home, where she wished to apologize to her

mother, Julia again passed in front of the tailor's shop. The black board was still in place and the shop curtained and closed. However, a side door stood ajar. This led through a passage to what was obviously a courtyard. Julia pushed the door wide enough to let her pass and then, almost furtively, made her way along the passage. She came to an outhouse, almost like a garden shed, which had a door with a frosted window.

Pushing this open, she saw a little man seated bow-legged on a long table. Steel-rimmed spectacles reposed on the tip of his sharp nose and he was stitching away while a gramophone at his elbow was playing a Chopin nocturne.

Julia's shadow passing in front of him revealed her presence. He said:

'If you have come to collect something, I have got the keys of the shop.'

'No,' she said. 'It is because of the black board. I wanted to know who was dead.'

'It's the Mama who is dead,' he answered. 'She was buttonholing in that armchair over there, the armchair in which she always worked. "Oh!" she said. "Oh, my!" and I thought maybe she was tired and was going to take a little nap, but after a while when she didn't move I went over to her, and she was dead. They are not back from Finchley yet.'

'Who is they?'

'The father and the two sons.'

'Why not you?' Julia queried.

'It worried me a bit having to go to a synagogue,' he said. 'I have never been in one. But I will go to Mass this evening at St Patrick's in Soho Square and pray there instead.'

'Does that mean you are Irish?'

'I'm from Cork,' he said. 'I just don't know what will happen to us all when they come back and Mama is no longer here.'

He remained seated with his feet tucked under him, stitching at a woman's jacket. Suddenly Julia bit her lip not to scream. She had just seen a tiny mouse impertinently climbing up a piece of brown holland of the kind tailors use to give body to a coat collar. The mouse was using it as a ladder. Catching the terror in the girl's eyes the little tailor looked from them to the mouse and said gently: 'You mustn't frighten the little lady, Dolly!'

'What!' cried Julia. 'You mean it is tame?'

'Tame as a mouse,' said the tailor. 'Everybody knows her. Even the cat wouldn't do her any harm.'

Julia steeled herself not to show her fear, but she retreated slowly to the door and said:

'When you see Richard will you tell him, please, that Julia came?'

'I'll tell him,' said the tailor.

As Julia emerged into the streets of Soho, she wondered if perhaps Mama had not had another reason for not wanting her son to marry Daisy. What a world separated them! Life was beginning to teach her that the path of lovers was strewn with complications.

On her return to the store, Julia found her superior in a sarcastic mood. 'You must have had a splendid lunch?' she said.

'I had no lunch at all,' said Julia. 'I called on a family where somebody had died, and I rushed home to apologize to Mother because I had been rude at breakfast, but she was out.'

'Oh!' said Betty, softened by this answer. 'Excuse me. I imagined that you had lunched with Mrs Davies. How did it go this morning?'

'It went very well. Mrs Topper said that the management had passed complimentary remarks about this department, and Mrs Davies more or less implied that it was largely due to you.'

Julia saw no reason to bring herself into the picture.

'Did she?' said Betty, smiling. 'What you tell me is very important, and explains why Mrs Davies has been so polite to me lately. Forgive me, Julia, for having been so unnecessarily jealous. I quite misunderstood the situation.'

Thus Betty, whose ill humour had so quickly dissolved under Julia's soft answer, went gaily off to her lunch, leaving Julia with time on her hands for the first time that day to turn her mind to a problem that greatly preoccupied her, the unfortunate love affair of Edith. Had it not been for Julia's busy morning in the store-room and her subsequent visit to Poland Street, she might have received either a visit or a message from Edith. As it was she was entirely without news. What, for instance, had happened in the course of that Sunday lunch with Edith's aunt?

Today was Monday, the start of yet another week. It was also the end of another month. September would soon be over. Julia gave a large part of her wages to her mother, keeping the remainder. Now that she had paid for the dress that Edith had put aside for her, this was not quite as much as she had hoped, but it was still nearly sufficient to allow her to buy the piece of squirrel that all the girls greatly wanted to possess. Edith had a lovely mink collar bought from her aunt's furrier, but if Julia managed to afford one like it her mother might feel that it would breed jealousy or ill will in their street. There were still pitfalls for a girl whose mother attached importance to the gossip of neighbours. The shortness of Julia's dress was a case in point. Even Betty was not free from parental criticism. Her local hairdresser had persuaded her to try a lighter colour rinse, which quite changed her appearance. Her parents, her father in particular, had been furious. When she had come down to Sunday lunch her father had stared at her in stony silence. Finally, his carving knife poised over the sirloin, he had turned to her mother and asked with that same icy sarcasm that Betty herself employed with Julia from time to time: 'Who is this person you have invited to lunch?'

Not that Julia felt any particular compassion for Betty in this ludicrous tale. Betty was not the sort of girl to stand stoutly by her girl friends if ever they got into trouble, whereas Julia would have gladly lied to help her friend Edith if ever Edith landed into a real scrape. Julia had this gift of getting on well with other girls. She might even have helped Betty if the situation were to warrant it. She had been schooled in this sort of thing by finding herself constantly involved in the quarrels, loves and intrigues of her mother's customers. Indeed, Julia loved listening to what was said in the confidence of dress fittings. She was born into feminine gossip as others are born into a love for motor cars or stamp collecting. Women seemed to her the tenderest, cruellest, most passionately interesting creatures in the world.

At teatime she found this note in her locker.

'Meet me without fail this evening. I am bursting with news. Terribly, terribly important. Edith.'

Well, she would just have to wait and see.

All the rest of the week Edith's affairs occupied the attention of all those who loved her. Julia and her mother could think of nothing else. Edith's uncle and aunt were radiantly happy. But none of them, not even Julia, was sufficiently naïve to suppose that considerable human problems would not be set in motion immediately. In all this Julia remained, as she had remained all along, a still inexperienced eighteen-year-old onlooker. It is questionable how much she understood at the time, how much she was able to piece together later when in turn, but not yet, a great love was to come to her.

Just as Archie, on first falling in love with Edith, had taken her to Regent's Park to meet Laura and the little girls, thus establishing a first contact with his family, so Edith, at her aunt's request, brought Archie back to her house to meet Uncle Esmond and herself. The same spontaneous sympathy sprang up between them as between Edith and Laura. From the aunt's point of view Archie was the ideal suitor for her niece's hand. If it had depended merely on her and on Uncle Esmond there would have been no shadow at all on the horizon. Financially, they were more than capable of doing as much for their niece as Archie's father was for his only son.

There remained, however, a vital obligation that Edith's

aunt insisted upon, and this was an immediate confrontation between Edith and her mother, preferably in Archie's presence. She argued that if Archie was the sort of man she took him to be, whatever emerged from such a confrontation could only work to the ultimate advantage of a really successful marriage.

Edith's mother was not the sort of woman to have allowed her principles to soften with the years. If she had been unable to give her elder daughter the smallest sign of forgiveness in the emotional atmosphere of a hospital ward there was little hope that now, after so many years of forbidding silence, she would have changed her mind. History, after all, was full of examples of both men and women who remained till their dying day stubborn to their principles. Edith's mother had not merely shown her disapproval openly in the ward. She had risen proudly and walked out of it.

Archie, therefore, was to call for Edith at 6 a.m. on Sunday and drive her to the house where she was born. As the weather continued in all the splendour of its Indian summer, the expedition promised to be like the foretaste of a honeymoon. They looked forward to it with immense excitement. It would be their first whole, long, wonderful day together.

Driving out of London at this early hour proved for Edith to be enchanting. Already she was beginning to think of the car as 'theirs', as their first home where they could be completely together, where they could talk of things nearest to their heart, where, when they wished to, they could hold hands, squeeze an arm or a finger. From time to time, however, Edith's thoughts went back to her mother.

'I was never the favourite daughter,' she said.

'Must there be a favourite?' said Archie.

'I think perhaps there must be. I was the one who disappointed. My younger sister, Florence, was the one who could never do anything wrong. But if Aunt Margaret is correctly informed, as I'm sure she is, Florence has married a man who has already stopped loving her and has virtually

248

turned Mother out of her own home. Does that strike you as strange?'

'Does it strike you as strange,' asked Archie, 'that in my parents' opinion (and in mine, too, for that matter) Laura should have made such an excellent match and that it should be proving so unhappy?'

'Aunt Margaret knows that Mother will never forgive me,' said Edith. 'Shall I tell you what she said to me?'

'Yes,' said Archie. 'Tell me.'

'She said: "You don't need to go as the repentant daughter. Be affectionate, but be dignified and remember that if you had not gone, and that if anything were to happen to your mother, you would never forgive yourself. Girls who end by making a success of their lives are generally the most sentimental. That means they suffer most." Then Aunt Margaret said this extraordinary thing. She said: "If I send you to your mother now, Edith, it is because you and I are much alike in character. For several years I was unable to forgive myself because I did not stretch out a helping hand to a girl when she needed it. It made me miserable. Fortunately I met her just in time on a cross-Channel steamer and she has become my favourite niece— almost my own daughter."'

'I already love your Aunt Margaret,' said Archie. 'Just as you love Laura. I thought we would have breakfast in an inn I know near Banbury. What would you say to that?'

'I would say porridge and fresh cream,' said Edith. 'Coffee, hot toast and marmalade.'

'Afterwards we will drive through the Shakespeare country in all the glory of early autumn,' said Archie. 'When we have finished with today's ordeal, I will drive you home and you can decide whether or not to leave the store.'

'Supposing you were to take a dislike to my mother? Supposing she were to say something terrible in your presence about me?'

'I told you a week ago,' said Archie, driving into the forecourt of the inn, 'I have grown up to be a man.'

.   .   .   .   .

She walked across the yard in front of him. She wore a two-piece and a bright red, polo-neck jumper. She had pinned up her jet black hair carefully the night before so that now its lustre added to what was exotic in her person. He thought her the most exquisite creature he had ever seen and wondered if she would help his own parents to forget their disappointment about Laura. It was not, of course, quite the moment to broach the subject of his marriage to them, but they were pleased about the success of his examinations, his real desire to join the firm and his obvious intention to be as enthusiastic and as enterprising as his father.

An hour and a half later they drove up to Edith's home. The house struck her as appearing smaller than when she had left it, but its familiar red roof and gabled front brought a lump in her throat. The garden smelt of dahlias, autumn daisies and damp leaves. They rang like strangers. A young woman with untidy hair and unable to hide her advanced pregnancy came to open the door. She looked unbelievingly at Edith, and then said in a flat, almost hostile voice: 'Oh, it's you!'

'Florence!' cried Edith, embracing her. 'This is my fiancé, Archie. Archie, my kid sister, Florence!'

When much later Edith described this homecoming to Julia, she said:

'What I wanted most was to see Mother. It had become an obsession with me. I kept on saying to Florence: "Where is mother?" When she came down her hair was white and she looked dreadfully tired. I fell at her feet and said: "Mother, I have brought you my fiancé, Archie. We are going to be married!"

'"Ah!" said my mother.

'"We are going to be married very simply, in a small church in the country. Will you say you are glad?"

'"What worries me," said my mother, "is that your sister Florence's marriage should have turned out so badly. What will happen to her when she has her baby? Dear

250

Florence, she was such a good girl, so pure, so loving and so honest."

'I got up to kiss her,' said Edith, 'but as my lips touched her forehead, I felt her whole body stiffening. I turned to Archie. He took my arm and we left. That was the moment when I knew that I really loved him, that we should love each other for ever.'

Julia said:

'How terrible—for mother and daughter to have to part like that, I mean.'

But she added quickly:

'Oh, Edith, I do so hope you will be happy for ever and ever.'

DATE DUE

GAYLORD   PRINTED IN U.S.A.